HIDE AND SEEK

Donna thought she had put Brodie Fox out of her life for good after he had deceived her so cruelly—but here he was again, blackmailing her into returning home again. Trying to force her into a reconciliation too—despite the fact that he was still as deeply involved as ever with the lovely Christabel!

HIDE AND SEEK

BY

CHARLOTTE LAMB

MILLS & BOON LIMITED
15–16 BROOK'S MEWS
LONDON W1A 1DR

First published in Great Britain 1987 by Mills & Boon Limited

© Charlotte Lamb 1987

Australian copyright 1987 Philippine copyright 1987 This edition 1987

ISBN 0 263 75617 3

Set in 10½ on 11½ pt. 01-0387-48198

Computer typeset by SB Datagraphics, Colchester, Essex

Printed and bound in Great Britain by Collins, Glasgow

CHAPTER ONE

DONNA first became aware that she was being followed when she turned the corner into the Boulevard Malesherbes and heard footsteps behind her immediately quicken. She'd been vaguely aware of someone behind her for several minutes without thinking too much about it. It was almost half past one in the morning; there were few other people about and almost no traffic. Suddenly realising that there was a man behind her who was running to catch up with her made the back of her neck prickle and she walked faster, too.

Marie-Louise had offered to drive her home, but she had cheerfully refused. 'No, thanks, I feel like a stroll! It's such a lovely night.'

'Don't you get nervous, walking through Paris in the middle of the night?' Marie-Louise had frowned. 'I really think I ought to drive you home, Donna.'

'After that bottle of Chablis? No, I think I'd be safer on my own two feet. At least you can't get arrested for drunken walking!'

Marie-Louise had laughed. 'Oh, I'm going to miss you! You must come and visit us whenever you can get to Lyons.'

'I will,' Donna had said before giving her a hug and walking away. She was going to miss Marie-Louise too. Paris would never be the same. People make places, and during the two years Donna had lived in Paris she had seen it through Marie-Louise's eyes and learnt to love it, to think of it as her second home—but as she quickened her footsteps now and heard the man behind her quicken his, the city seemed suddenly hostile.

For the first time she regretted the silence in the streets where she lived. She had fallen in love with the Boulevard Malesherbes the first time she saw it. It had been a hot August Sunday afternoon; little traffic on the road, no shops open and most of the apartments empty. In August, Parisians flood out of town for *les vacances* by the sea or in the country, but Donna hadn't realised that the day she first came to the Boulevard Malesherbes. She had stood under the plane trees watching their shadowed leaves flickering on to the pavement, staring at the tall shuttered houses drowsing in the heat like a row of grey cats, enchanted by the atmosphere.

She had taken the apartment she had come to see although the rent was higher than she had intended to pay, rather more than she could afford, in fact. But she had never regretted it, especially after she had begun to make friends and settle down.

Now, though, she became very aware of the deep silence broken only by the tap of her high heels and the echoing click of the heels coming closer behind her.

The Boulevard was wide and shadowy, especially under the trees. Donna looked up at the shutters and knew that most of the apartments behind them were empty now, this August, as they had been that first August. In that month Paris belongs to the tourist, before whose locust advance the French retreat in disgust.

If the man behind her caught up with her and she screamed, would anyone hear? Donna suddenly crossed the road obliquely, running. The man behind her broke into a run, too, but she was now within a few yards of the door of the apartment building. She could see the brass gleam of the doorknob, she put on speed and reached it with a gasp of relief.

Only then did she realise that the man following her had vanished. She glanced round, hearing the silence, the absence of other footsteps. The Boulevard was empty; the lamplight gleamed, the shadows of leaves flickered on the road around each lamp. There was nobody else in the street but herself.

Far from making her feel easier, that alarmed her into diving inside the building. The concierge was dozing over her table, behind her lace curtains. She started, head jerking back and Donna gave her a wave as she went past. *'C'est moi, madame. Bonne nuit.'*

It made her feel safer to know that Madame Lebrun was keeping a wary eye on anyone who went in or out. When Madame wasn't at her post, Monsieur Lebrun took over from her.

Donna's apartment was on the fourth floor. There was no lift. She had to climb the narrow stairs, which seemed to take for ever. In the first months of living here she had lost pounds. Tonight she was tensely conscious of the fact that the apartments she passed on her climb were all empty. The other tenants had left two weeks ago; they would be back when *la rentrée* started, the weekend at the beginning of September when everyone came back to the city.

This time of the year was Donna's favourite month. Her part of Paris was so still and peaceful in August; tourists didn't flock to Malesherbes, the closest they came was to the Boulevard Haussmann, to the great shops: Printemps, Galeries Lafayette, and C & A. That was a mere few minutes' walk from Malesherbes, yet it might have been another planet. Paris was a city of villages bordering each other but sharply separated.

Unlocking her front door, Donna hurriedly switched on the light in the corridor and listened. The apartment seemed silent, empty. Yet she still felt nervous. She went quickly through the rooms, switching on all the lights. Nothing had been disturbed, there was no sign of an intruder. Relaxing, she closed the front door and went into the tiny kitchen to make herself some hot chocolate to take to bed.

She was just stirring the milk into the mug when the phone began to ring.

She jumped. The shrill sound seemed very loud in the silent flat. Hurrying into the sitting-room, she grabbed up the phone, wondering who on earth could be ringing her at this hour of the night.

'Donna?' The voice was male, low, distinctly English.

'Yes?' She was instantly on her guard, her nerves prickling.

'It's me, Gavin.'

Donna's expression changed; her eyes widening in surprise. 'Gavin? Where are you? Do you know what time it is? It's two in the morning here. Is something wrong?'

'Are you alone?' Gavin asked in a whisper, and she frowned.

'Of course I'm alone. I . . .'

'Has anyone rung you from London?' he interrupted. 'Have you heard from anyone today?'

'Gavin, what on earth are you talking about? What's

happened? Why should anyone ring me from London?'

'Never mind,' said Gavin in a strangely dry voice. 'Look, I'm coming to your apartment now—will you tell that woman to let me in?'

'The concierge?' Donna's mind was working slowly, she was so tired. 'Yes, of course—do you mean you're in Paris? You're here now?'

'I'm in a telephone box just up the road. I wanted to be sure the coast was clear. I'll explain when I see you; in five minutes.'

He rang off and Donna automatically put down the phone, then picked it up to ring the concierge to warn her that Gavin would be arriving any minute. Without warning, Madame Lebrun wouldn't let him past her. She often refused to admit male visitors after ten o'clock at night, even when they were respectable middle-aged men like Donna's boss and even if they were accompanied by their wives. This was a respectable house, she always said flatly. The landlord didn't like all this coming and going at night.

'*Votre frère, mademoselle?*' Madame repeated suspiciously with one of her loud sniffs. Donna could imagine her expression; dourly cynical.

'*Oui, vraiment! C'est mon jumeau.*'

'*Ah, oui,*' Madame said reluctantly, remembering then that Donna had a twin brother who had visited her before. She couldn't doubt the relationship because the likeness was unmistakable. Donna and Gavin weren't identical twins, of course, merely fraternal, but they still resembled each other enough for a stranger to spot the fact that they were twins when they were together.

Madame grimly agreed to let Gavin into the house and Donna hung up and drank her hot chocolate

quickly. There was no point in thinking about getting
ready for bed now. She frowned anxiously as she waited
for his knock. Why had he arrived without warning in
the middle of the night? It was true that she had been
out all evening, having dinner with Marie-Louise in her
apartment, but why hadn't Gavin rung earlier that
day?

He knew very well that she usually went out in the
evenings—to see a play or film, go to a party, meet
people for dinner. She had a wide circle of friends in
Paris—half a dozen of them would be driving up to
Lyons together for Marie-Louise's wedding next week.
They planned to make a long weekend of it and stay at a
motel on the city outskirts.

Marie-Louise was marrying a man she had known
most of her life. Their families were old friends; it was
almost an arranged match, except that they were very
much in love. When Donna first heard how eager
Marie-Louise's family were for the marriage to take
place, she had been disturbed.

'Don't let them stampede you into anything!' she had
warned. 'It never works, that sort of marriage. It almost
happened to me once—my father wanted me to marry
someone and I almost did, but I came to my senses in
time. You have to stand up to that sort of pressure.
After all, it's your life, not theirs!'

Marie-Louise had laughed affectionately at her. 'You
think I'm crazy? I'm glad my parents are happy about
it, but I'd marry him whatever they thought. There's
never been anyone else for me—and Jean-Paul feels the
same.'

Donna hadn't been convinced until she met Jean-
Paul and saw the way he smiled at Marie-Louise. They

were so radiantly in love that it made her heart ache
with envy. It hadn't been that way for her.

She absent-mindedly washed up her mug and hung it
back in the cupboard, listening intently for the sound of
Gavin's arrival. She had a very uneasy feeling that he
brought bad news.

The doorbell rang sharply and she went to answer it.
'Gavin! You choose the funniest times to drop in!'

He smiled at her, wearily leaning on the doorpost.
'Sorry. Are you as tired as I feel?'

He looked more than tired; he looked crumpled and
exhausted, a thin figure in a lightweight suit, his tie
undone, his collar open. He was carrying an overnight
bag in one hand and she got an instant impression of
someone running—from what?

'Well, come on in, you're always welcome, you know
that. Any time, day or night.' She took his bag, her
anxiety deepening. Had he quarrelled with their
father? Had he been thrown out of the house for good
this time?

He followed her into the sitting-room and threw
himself into a chair, closing his eyes with a long sigh.
'God, I feel like death!'

'You don't look too well,' she said, watching his
drawn face. They were both fine-boned, fair-skinned,
fair-haired. On Donna that bone structure and colouring was ultra-feminine; made men's heads turn in the
street, Gavin didn't have that effect on women. He was
oddly colourless, his features weak, his manner
unimpressive.

'Has something happened?' she asked him. She
understood Gavin instinctively, they had a form of
telepathy; after all, they were twins.

It was working overtime now. She hadn't had any premonition that he was in trouble, but the minute she heard his voice she had picked up tension and uneasiness. Gavin was frightened. About what?

'I've been a fool,' he said, opening his eyes to look at her warily.

Donna smiled. 'So what's new in that?'

His grin was mere pretence. 'God, I'm tired. I came over on the ferry from Dover and got lost on the road from Calais.'

'How on earth did you do that? Didn't you use the *péage*?'

'I got lost after I left the motorway. I stopped and rang you, but I'd forgotten your number and whoever answered didn't make sense. You know my French is terrible. So I pushed on to Paris, but when I got here you were out and your concierge wouldn't let me in to wait for you. I hung about waiting for a while, but a gendarme gave me a funny look so I felt I'd better go and have a snack while I waited.'

She frowned. 'Were you out in the street just now?' I heard someone running behind me but when I looked round, he'd gone.'

Gavin sat up, a tic beating beside his mouth. 'Someone was following you?'

'It wasn't you? No, I suppose if it had been you'd have caught up with me.' She looked sharply at him, alarmed by his expression. 'Gavin, what are you frightened of?'

'I'm in bad trouble, Donna,' he muttered, very pale. 'And he's found out. I had to get away before all hell broke loose.'

'He? Who are you talking about? Father?'

He shook his head, his mouth turning down at the edges. 'Brodie, but he's going to tell Father, so it comes to the same thing.'

Donna's face became paper-white. She might have known that Brodie Fox was mixed up in this somewhere. She looked searchingly at her brother. 'What have you done, Gavin?' But she was already beginning to guess; she knew him too well.

He caught her glance and bit his lip. 'I was desperate for money, Donna. I'd got into a run of bad luck, but I was sure it was going to change—it couldn't go on for ever and all I needed was a chance to win back everything I'd lost.'

'Oh, Gavin,' she groaned, flinching as if he'd hit her. 'Gambling again after you'd promised faithfully . . .'

'You don't know what my life's like,' he burst out furiously. 'You're okay, you're out of it, but I'm stuck there. Day after day the same thing—the office, the boredom of that desk, the stupid people nagging at me all the time. And Father, looking at me with that expression on his face, as if he wishes I'd never been born.'

Donna knelt down beside his chair as he buried his face in his hands, shivering violently as if he had a chill. A long lock of blond hair trailed over his fingers and she brushed it back with a sigh.

'Don't, Gavin.' If he started to cry she wouldn't be able to bear it. He was a man now, he wasn't a little boy, but he was still so helpless, he had come to her because he didn't know what else to do.

'Help me, Donna,' he whispered, as he always had.

'Of course I will,' she promised, stroking his hair. Although they were the same age exactly she had always felt she was older. Even as a child, Gavin had been in need of her protection, he had always been the weaker of the two, perhaps because he was born second, half an hour after Donna, and had almost died. He had been rushed to an incubator and watched closely for the first week. In some ways Gavin had needed to be watched ever since.

'How did Brodie find out that you'd been gambling?' she asked him.

'I'd borrowed from the private account,' he said, his face hidden behind his hands.

Her face tightened in shock. 'Gavin! From Father's account? But you said it was Brodie who found out . . .'

'Brodie runs the firm now,' Gavin said bitterly, his hands dropping to show her a face pale with angry emotion. 'Father handed over control in the spring. He hasn't been well for a long time.'

'What's the matter with him?' Donna asked urgently. She was getting shock after shock tonight. She'd had no idea that her father was ill or that he no longer ran the family firm.

'Angina,' Gavin said shortly. 'Don't look so worried—it isn't as serious as it sounds. He has to take it easy, that's all. He only gets attacks when he's upset or overtired. His doctor advised retirement at once, but Father wasn't ready to give up altogether, so he appointed Brodie Managing Director and became Chairman. He comes in for board meetings and keeps an eye on what's happening from a distance.'

'So Brodie Fox runs the firm now?' Donna's mouth took on a cynical curve. He hadn't had to marry her to get what he wanted, after all. Wasn't that nice for him?

'You sound surprised!' Gavin said bitterly.

'No, I'm not surprised at all.' Her voice was flat, careful.

'Nor was I. He's been after control ever since he joined the firm. Father's last attack was his big chance.'

'Why didn't you tell me before?' asked Donna, staring at him. 'You were over here in the spring.'

He looked away shiftily and her frown deepened. 'I didn't want to upset you.'

She didn't quite believe him; Gavin was a bad liar. Slowly she asked, 'How much did you take, Gavin?'

He moistened his lips, still not meeting her eyes. 'I meant to put it back, you know. I was sure my luck was about to change; it couldn't get worse, I thought.'

'How much, Gavin?'

'I took a thousand,' he muttered, and she made a face. Did she have that much in her savings account?

'I might be able to raise a thousand,' she thought aloud, and Gavin glanced at her and away.

'That wasn't all, you see, I . . .'

Her breath caught. 'You borrowed more than a thousand? How much more?'

'Don't get angry with me!' Gavin protested, flinching. 'You know Father keeps me short of money. He treats me like a schoolboy, doles out little sums when he feels like it. If I worked for anyone else I'd earn far more than I do—and after all, one day the firm will be mine.' He stopped, gave her a quick look. 'Ours, I meant. You know Father's will leaves it to both of us equally.' His face had become petulant, aggrieved. 'All that money lying there and one day it's going to be mine, why can't he give me more now? I wouldn't have had to take it if he hadn't been so tight-fisted.'

Donna couldn't speak for a second; his attitude

appalled her. He talked as if their father had no right to keep his money, as if he couldn't wait for Father to die.

'Gavin,' she whispered, shaking her head. 'Oh, Gavin, sometimes I . . .' She broke off as his weak mouth quivered. He hated to be reproached or blamed. The only influence she had with him was that he knew she loved him in spite of his faults, and if she began to be too critical Gavin would stop confiding in her. She had to hide her shock and distress.

'How much do you need?' she asked him patiently.

He still looked sullen. 'Sixteen thousand.'

Her head swam, as if she was about to faint. She had never dreamt it would be that much. The sum was wildly beyond her reach. They had each inherited a legacy from their dead mother on their twenty-first birthday. Donna had used her money to move to Paris, pay a deposit on this apartment and her fees at language school until she was fluent enough in French to be able to get a job as a translator. She knew Gavin had simply gambled away his money.

She took a harsh breath. 'Gavin, I haven't even got sixteen thousand pounds!'

His face broke up in tremors of pleading and agitation. 'If you talked to Brodie . . .'

'No!' she broke out, shuddering. She had promised herself that she would never set eyes on Brodie again, and even to help Gavin she couldn't face the thought of it.

'You don't understand,' Gavin said desperately. 'If he tells Father, I'm finished, he'll cut me out of the will. He told me so last time.' He broke off, looking at her, then away—first red, then white. 'Donna, I know you must despise me, but I get so depressed because I can't please Father however hard I try, and that makes me feel so low. I have to get away, and gambling is the only way I know of forgetting everything else. When you're at the tables, that's the whole world. You shut out all the problems. I've often thought that war must be like that. Suddenly all your worries seem tiny. You just have to concentrate on staying alive. That's what it feels like when I'm gambling—every spin is life or death.'

She stared at him, shaken by the sudden outburst. He had never been so frank with her before, but he had made a sort of twisted sense. Their father was partly to blame—he was too cold a man, his standards too high, his attitudes too rigid. He despised Gavin because his son wasn't made in his image, and he had never hidden that contempt. No wonder Gavin was prone to bouts of despair and tried to sink his worries at the roulette table!

She got up and ruffled his fair hair gently. 'Why don't you go to bed now? In the morning we'll see what can be done. I'll help you, don't worry.'

Some of the tension went out of his drawn face and he sighed, getting up too. 'Thanks, Donna.' He gave her a hug. 'What would I do if I didn't have you to run to?'

Would he learn to rely on himself? she wondered sadly, but knew that she couldn't risk such an experiment in case Gavin went to pieces altogether. Their mother had died when they were very small, and Donna had been all the mother he had ever known.

He gave a smothered yawn. 'You're right, I am tired. Where's my overnight bag?' He picked it up from the chair where she had placed it. 'Any chance of a cup of hot milk?'

'Of course, get into bed and I'll bring it to you.'

He grinned faintly at her, brushing that stray lock of fair hair out of his eyes. 'Could you show the brandy to it? I need a pick-me-up.'

She smiled, nodding, and watched him walk wearily down the corridor to the tiny boxroom she used as a second bedroom.

She heated the milk and added a finger of brandy, and Gavin had undressed and was in bed when she tapped at his door.

She put the milk on the bedside table, smiling down at his pallid face. 'Try to sleep. I won't be going to work tomorrow, of course, as it's a Saturday. Do you want me to wake you or let you sleep?'

'You'd better wake me by nine, if I haven't got up by then,' he said ruefully. 'Donna, I've been thinking— you said someone followed you tonight? Did you see who it was?'

'No, but I got the feeling it was a man. It can't have anything to do with you, Gavin. It was probably just a prowler who decided not to jump me.'

'I suppose so,' Gavin said slowly, frowning. 'I'm edgy, that's all. I had an interview with Brodie this morning. He told me he'd uncovered the amount I'd borrowed—he had the nerve to call me a thief, damn him! He told me he was going to speak to Father on Monday morning before the board meeting. He said he'd give me the weekend to tell Father myself, but he knew I wouldn't be able to face it. I saw his face; that look—the way Father looks at me. Brodie despises me too. I walked out of there knowing I had to run, and I think Brodie knew, too. All the way here I've felt sure he was behind me.'

Donna stared at him fixedly. His face had a peculiar greenish tinge. He looked the way he had looked as a child when he was in trouble; Gavin had usually been sick with nerves when Father was angry with him.

'Stop thinking about it,' she ordered, trying to sound calm. 'You won't sleep if you keep brooding.'

'Brooding over Brodie!' he said, laughing on the edge of hysteria. 'How can I help it?' He picked up the glass of milk in both hands, sipping it. 'I'll be okay. Sorry to keep you up, Donna. I'll see you in the morning.'

He was looking slightly better already. He had handed his problem to her. Donna gave him a wry smile and went out. She wasn't going to find it so easy to sleep. How dared Brodie call him a thief? Gavin shouldn't have taken that money, but at least he was one of the family, Brodie Fox wasn't. He had walked into the firm five years ago with the set intention of taking it over if he could. What right did he have to talk to Gavin like that?

She undressed and got into bed, her head throbbing. In the darkness her bedroom seemed unfamiliar; as if Gavin's appearance so suddenly had changed her world.

He had been here before, several times. Her father had never visited Paris since Donna moved there, but Gavin had. She hadn't been back to England since she left it; she didn't want to run any risk of seeing Brodie and knew that if she went home her father was quite capable of producing Brodie without warning.

She turned over, sighing heavily. What was she going to do about Gavin? She had promised to help him, but how? She wasn't going on her knees to Brodie Fox. She would rather die. That would feed his ego, wouldn't it?

He would love that, having her at his mercy, watching her beg.

Two years ago she had told him what she thought of him before she left for good. She hadn't minced words, or disguised her contempt, and he had watched her with icy blue eyes, not a shred of expression in his face.

She had been armoured against the threat of his presence then; if she had to go to him to plead for her brother she would be defenceless. But she couldn't think any more tonight. She must sleep. She turned over again, her body hot and aching. It was a very warm night; the sheets clung to her skin. How was she going to get any rest when her mind wouldn't stop working?

It was another half-hour before she finally unwound enough to relax, and when she woke up the room was full of sunlight and the smell of coffee. Surprised, she realised Gavin must be up already.

She stumbled out of bed, yawning. It was nearly nine. She felt as if she had barely closed her eyes, but she must have had five hours' sleep. She pulled on a cotton night-robe and tied the wide satin belt before going to the kitchen, where she found her brother making coffee and squeezing oranges.

He gave her a wry smile. 'Good morning. Did you sleep?'

'Not too well. How about you?' Her eyes searched his face. 'You look better.'

'I slept like a log,' he admitted. 'And now I'm starving—is there any bread? I can't find it.'

'I've run out. I'll have to get some from the *boulangerie* down the street.'

'I'll go,' he said. 'Tell me where it is.'

'Turn left at the next corner and you'll see it across the road. Get some croissants and rolls and a baton loaf.' As he turned to go she asked, 'Got some French money?' and Gavin nodded.

'Keep the coffee hot, I won't be a minute.'

The front door slammed behind him, and Donna drifted slowly towards the bathroom. She splashed cold water on her face, brushed her tousled hair and assessed her reflection with a grimace. Her green eyes were smudged with shadows of weariness, her blonde hair seemed lifeless, her skin was pale.

'You look terrible,' she told herself.

The doorbell rang and she sighed. Gavin had come back sooner than she had expected.

'You were quick,' she said, opening the door, then froze in shock as she saw the man outside.

Donna would have slammed the door shut again if he hadn't pushed his way into the apartment while she was still thinking about it.

'What are you doing here?' she protested, and got a smile of dry cynicism.

'Where's Gavin?' He walked into the sitting-room and looked around, his eyes curious. She had furnished it from sales and second-hand shops, picking up solid pieces of furniture from between the wars, not quite antiques yet still made by craftsmen and intended to last. The room had a late twenties feel to it; even the ornaments were in period.

'Gavin?' Donna fenced, and got another of his crooked little smiles.

'Don't play the innocent, it doesn't suit you.'

He had eyes like blue ice, deep-set and faintly hooded by heavy lids. A tall man, he was frighteningly self-

contained, impossible to outthink. She felt an angry
need to see him lose his temper, to watch some sort of
emotion wrecking that calm certainty.

'I know he's here,' he said, walking past her. 'I
discovered that he'd skipped the country yesterday
afternoon and I got a Paris detective agency to check to
see if he'd come here.'

'You had my apartment watched?' she snapped as he
glanced into the kitchen. 'How dare you?'

He gave her a dry sideways smile. 'Don't talk like a
melodrama, Miss Cowley. There was no point in my
following him to Paris if he hadn't come here. I never
waste time on red herrings.'

'I suppose that it was your peeping Tom who
followed me home last night? He was lucky I didn't call
the police!'

Brodie shrugged. 'Breakfast for two, I see,' he
commented, eyeing the table Gavin had laid before he
went to buy bread. 'Gavin still in bed? Or have you got
a lover in your bedroom?' His smile mocked her.

'Yes,' Donna said coolly, and for once caught him by
surprise. She saw his blue eyes harden. His colouring
was dramatic—tanned skin, dark eyes, black hair.
Raven black, she thought. What other plumage for a
bird of prey?

'That's a lie,' he said tersely, lids lowered.

She smiled; a taunt in her eyes. 'I wouldn't advise
you to check—he might teach you better manners.'

She saw the glacial anger in his face with satisfaction. She might not be able to draw blood, but at least
she had inflicted a pinprick.

As she had known he would, he turned on his heel
and strode down the corridor to the bedroom. Donna

ran into the sitting-room, unfastened the high windows
and stepped out on to the balcony that overlooked the
street. For a second she thought she was too late to
catch Gavin, but then she saw him coming, swinging
casually under the plane trees with his arms piled with
food. He had stopped to buy fruit, too; she saw a
watermelon balanced on top of a bag full of croissants.
Leaning over the ironwork railing, she was just going to
call a warning, when a hand suddenly fastened over her
mouth. She shot a startled look backward; Brodie's
face was behind her shoulder. He pulled her, struggling, back into the room.

She tried to bite his hand and he whirled her
sideways until she was arched helplessly over his arm,
her eyes spitting rage at him above the hand silencing
her.

'You're cleverer than your brother,' Brodie said
coolly. 'You had me fooled for a minute, until I heard
you scampering in here and realised you'd sent me on a
wild goose chase.'

Donna mumbled furiously against his hand, tried to
kick him. The doorbell rang and Brodie gave her a
mocking smile.

'Too late. He's here.' She found herself being
propelled toward the front door, still gagged by
Brodie's hand. He only released her at the last minute,
then pulled the door open after he had pushed her
behind him.

'Come in, Gavin,' said Brodie, and over his shoulder
Donna saw her brother's face grow white and stiff with
shock.

CHAPTER TWO

THE watermelon wobbled and fell, bouncing off down the corridor. Donna chased it; that gave her time to think. She couldn't let Brodie bully Gavin, she had to separate them somehow. She heard Gavin edge into the kitchen with Brodie following him like a cat after a mouse with no hole to go to—by the time she joined them her brother had collapsed into a chair and Brodie was looming over him, talking softly. She caught the tail end of a sentence. '. . . won't get away with it. This time you're going to face the consequences of what you've done.'

Donna dropped the dark green watermelon on to the table with a thud. Brodie looked up; their eyes met as if over crossed swords.

'I want to talk to you in the sitting-room,' she said tersely.

'Later.'

'Now!' She was bristling with rage, but it didn't cause so much as a ripple in that controlled face.

'I'm talking to your brother,' he said calmly, dismissively.

The arrogance made her teeth meet. Through them, she hissed, 'Who the hell do you think you are? You work for my father. You don't employ either me or my brother, so don't talk to me like that.'

'I work for your father, not for you, Miss Cowley,' he said with a dry smile, his eyes narrowed as he

24

deliberately emphasised her name.

Hot colour burnt in her face, her chin went up. 'What right do you have to play detective, follow my brother all the way to Paris, force your way into my apartment and use threats and physical violence on me?'

Gavin looked up. 'What did he do to you, Sis?' he asked angrily.

'Manhandled me.'

Donna was still staring at Brodie; she saw his mouth compress. 'I stopped you warning your brother that I was here—it hardly comes under the heading of grievous bodily harm.'

'Keep your filthy hands off my sister!' Gavin told him aggressively, beginning to get up.

Brodie put one hand on his shoulder. Donna watched with a sense of shock as he exerted enough pressure to force Gavin back into his chair. The little defeat made Gavin go white again; this time with humiliation.

'Don't get into a fight with me, Gavin. You'd lose.' It wouldn't have made Gavin wince so much if the older man's voice hadn't been calm; almost gentle.

'Why don't you pick on someone your own size, then?' Donna muttered.

'You, for instance?' For a second she saw a gleam of amusement in his cold blue eyes, then it was gone. 'This wasn't the way I'd planned to spend my weekend,' he said drily. 'Following your brother across the channel wasn't a game, Miss Cowley. I could have saved myself all this time and trouble by doing one of two things. I could just have told your father that his son had embezzled a large sum from the private account, or called in the police without bothering your father. If the thief had been anyone but your father's son that's what

I would have done. Your father isn't supposed to
involve himself in the day-to-day running of the firm
any more, especially if it might upset him.' He paused,
eyeing her grimly. 'I decided to deal with the whole
problem myself without involving the police, and as
your brother had skipped the country I had to cancel
my plans for the weekend and follow him.'

'I'm sure my father will be very grateful to you,' said
Donna, thrusting her hands into the pockets of her
cotton robe. 'On the other hand, if you hadn't scared
my brother senseless he wouldn't have run away. You
wanted *him* to go to my father, didn't you? If that had
caused a fatal heart attack *you* couldn't be blamed.'

His face tightened. 'My one concern is to make sure
your father *doesn't* have another attack!'

She laughed disbelievingly. 'Do you expect us to
believe that? You're determined to make sure he knows
about the money Gavin took. You want him to turn
against Gavin and cut him out of his will. That would
leave you sitting prettily waiting to move in once my
father was dead.'

'If I wanted that, I could just have told him. I
wouldn't have followed Gavin here.' He had himself on
a tight rein again, but he was angry, she was glad to see,
and she smiled again, eyes cynical.

'Oh, I think you're shrewd enough to work out that it
would put you in a very good light if you galloped after
Gavin and brought him home to face the music before
you broke the sad news to my father!'

'You have a devious mind, Miss Cowley.'

Suddenly her temper snapped. 'Don't keep calling
me that!' She wished she hadn't lost her cool a second
later when she saw the glint in his eyes.

'Sorry, I had the impression I wasn't allowed to call you Donna any more.'

She looked across at her brother, too angry to be capable of answering Brodie. 'Eat your breakfast, Gavin, while I have a word with *him* in the sitting-room.' She lifted the coffee-pot and poured her brother a cup of black coffee, handed it to him, walked past and out of the door without looking to see if Brodie was going to follow her.

She heard him behind her after a brief hesitation. She watched him walk into the sitting-room and closed the door. Brodie turned to face her, his long body tensely at rest the way a panther waits in the darkness of the jungle; every muscle poised for the spring to kill and yet very still. He frightened her, although she wouldn't let him see it. She watched him, frowning, wondering how to get through to him.

'If you really care about my father, you won't tell him what Gavin has done,' she began, and saw his mouth tighten.

'Sixteen thousand pounds is missing from the accounts—how do you propose I hide that fact without incriminating myself?'

'Give me a few days and I'll see that the money is replaced,' she said huskily. She didn't know how she was going to get it, but she would move heaven and earth to do it.

Brodie folded his arms, considering her as if she were a new species he had never come across before. 'You have that much money immediately to hand?'

'I'll get it.'

'Borrow it from someone, you mean?'

'Does it matter how I'll get it, so long as I do?'

'Yes, I think it does,' he said. 'The money has to be replaced by Tuesday.'

Her lips went dry. 'Tuesday? Can't you give me more time than that?'

His brows rose. 'You don't understand—the official audit takes place on Tuesday and that money must be back by then.'

'Couldn't you explain that . . .' Her voice broke off and he bent towards her, his face ironic.

'Yes?'

'I don't know,' she muttered. 'You must think of something.'

'Lie for you, you mean?' he enquired, and her face flushed again.

'Do you have to put it like that?'

'I was merely trying to define our terms. I want to know what you're asking me to do.'

'Surely you can stall the auditors for a few days just until I get the money?'

He walked slowly to the couch and sat down, crossing his legs. Donna bitterly noted the quality of his pale grey suit. It must have cost the earth. The shirt was pale silk; a lucent blue which echoed the colour of his eyes, and the dove-grey tie was silk too. Brodie's taste had always been good; he liked the best and now he could afford it. He had climbed the mountain and he meant to stay there, whatever he had to do to make sure of it.

'Suppose I did as you asked?' he said quietly. 'You won't ever get that money back from Gavin, you know. He'll be full of gratitude for a few days, then he'll put it all out of his mind. He doesn't like to remember things that make him feel a failure.'

'That's my business!'

'In a way it's mine, too. In a few months he'll be gambling again—he's compulsive, he can't stop. It's a sickness and it ought to be treated as one, but your father prefers to believe that all Gavin has to do is make up his mind to stop—he won't admit that there's anything wrong with Gavin.'

Her green eyes held a darkness. She didn't want him to understand Gavin so well, she resented his shrewdness. It alarmed her for reasons of her own. Brodie waited, then went on, 'Sooner or later he'll need money desperately enough to steal again, but this time it won't be from the firm because I have no intention of allowing him anywhere near any large sums of money in future. And if he steals from someone else, it won't be so easy to cover up next time.'

'There won't be a next time,' Donna denied angrily. 'And you must be crazy if you plan to push Gavin out of the firm—have you forgotten that one day he'll own it?'

'I didn't say I wanted him out of the firm—only that from now on he can't be allowed access to money. He won't be able to siphon cash out of the private account again.'

She laughed furiously. 'Who do you think you are? My family run that company—you just work for them. How dare you talk as if my brother were some junior clerk caught with his fingers in the till?'

Brodie's steady gaze didn't falter. 'That's what he is—and if he weren't Gavin Cowley I'd have called the police by now. Do you think that's fair? One law for Gavin and another for any other employee?'

Donna bit her lip. 'Gavin wasn't really stealing, he was taking money which he knew was . . .'

'His father's? You think that's morally acceptable?'
His lip curled and she flinched.

'Of course not.' She turned away and walked to the
window, aware that he watched her, his eyes wandering. Their assessment made her self-conscious, and that
made her angry again.

She swung round. 'You don't intend Gavin to be any
threat to you, do you? If he's allowed to stay on he'll be
given a sinecure—a peripheral job where he can be
forgotten while you really run things.'

'Do you think Gavin could run the firm?' Brodie
shrugged those firmly muscled shoulders. 'Within two
years the company would be bankrupt and the staff
would be out of work. Or don't they count? Are you
happy to see them out on the streets looking for new
jobs?'

She laughed shortly. 'Oh, you're clever, I grant you
that. And lucky too. Gavin has played right into your
hands, hasn't he? You didn't have to get rid of him, he
did it for you.'

Brodie got up and she backed, gripping the window-
sill. On his feet he was disturbingly tall, potentially
dangerous, especially when his hard-boned features
took on the look they wore at the moment—an icy
impatience in the blue eyes, the mouth reined and the
jaw rigid.

'Perhaps we can cut out the insults if you've got some
of the poison out of your system,' he said through his
teeth. 'The real question is—what are we going to do
about Gavin now?'

'We?' she threw back, her eyes rejecting the plural.

Brodie took two steps and was far too near her. Her

body arched instinctively away from him, her chin
defiant.

'Don't keep fighting me, Donna,' he said quietly,
watching her.

Her mouth quivered. 'Oh, you'd like me to be putty
in your hands, I suppose!'

The blue eyes flashed and she caught a ripple of
expression in that tanned face. It alarmed her,
especially when he smiled slowly.

'What an interesting picture.'

'Forget it!' She was husky with fury.

He was even closer now, his hands shot out and
grasped the window-sill on each side of her. Donna
found herself trapped and looked at him nervously.

'What do you think you're doing?'

His face brooded; the blue eyes very dark, the mouth
level. 'What went wrong, Donna?' he asked suddenly.
'Why did you turn against me like that? What did I do?'

Her eyes shifted, her colour ebbed and flowed, her
breathing became erratic and her heart beat frighteningly fast. Why did he still have this effect on her? She
had thought she was cured, she had believed he was
nothing to her but an enemy, a man she must be wary of
and watch carefully. It was worrying to feel those
physical reactions to his nearness. Her body remembered things she wanted only to forget.

'I don't want to talk about the past,' she said, not
meeting his eyes.

'I do.' His body shifted, he was almost touching her,
the muscular firmness of his thighs an inch away.

'I don't care what you want,' Donna muttered,
staring at his grey tie. This close she could pick up the
cool fragrance of his after-shave, the warm scent of his

skin, muskier, more disturbing.

'Don't you?' His voice had dropped to a murmured intimacy that did crazy things to her heartbeat.

'Don't waste your time flirting with me,' she said fiercely.

'You're very tanned, It makes your hair like silvery silk.' His hand came up to touch her hair and she jerked away like a frightened horse, tossing her head to dislodge his hand.

'Don't touch me!'

'You used to like me to touch you,' he said in that soft, seductive voice, and her throat closed up. She had forgotten how convincing he could be; if she didn't know better she might almost believe that the look in his eyes was genuine attraction, not the mimicry of a shrewd operator who saw her as his insurance policy if his other plans didn't work out.

'What are you scared of, Donna?'

'Not of you, never of you,' she said feverishly, and saw his smile with dismay, wishing she had sounded more in command of herself. He picked up every tiny signal like a Geiger counter sensing radioactivity. She must learn to disguise her feelings better.

'We were talking about my brother!' she said sharply, twisting her body free. Brodie didn't try to stop her. He swivelled to watch her cross the room, her limbs not quite in control, her breathing far too fast.

'Gavin needs treatment,' he answered calmly as she sat down on a chair. 'He ought to see a psychiatrist. Gambling is a symptom of a deeper problem.'

Donna was surprised by his insight. She couldn't argue with that, it was what she had come to think herself. Brodie leaned against the window-sill, his body casual. 'I've tried several times to convince your father that Gavin is sick, but he has nineteenth-century attitudes towards any form of mental illness. He's afraid of the stigma attached to it. He simply loses his temper if I raise the matter. He seems to believe I'm telling him that Gavin isn't sane, he doesn't recognise depression and compulsive behaviour as an illness. But when he hears that Gavin has taken this money, he may begin to realise that I am right.'

Slowly Donna said, 'Especially if he has to choose between having a son with criminal tendencies, and a son who is only sick and needs medical help?'

'Exactly.' Brodie strolled towards her and sat down again on the couch, facing her. 'And it would help if you were there to add your opinion to mine.'

She stiffened. 'No!'

'If we talked to him together we might have more effect,' Brodie went on, ignoring her protest.

'You know I haven't spoken to my father for two years, and anyway, he wouldn't listen to me. He never did. Your opinion counts far more with him than mine.' There was bitterness in her voice as she finished speaking and her mouth was quivering. Her father had hurt her two years ago; she hadn't forgiven him yet. He had been duped by Brodie Fox too, and when the scales fell from her eyes she hadn't been able to persuade her father how wrong they had both been about Brodie.

'If you really care about Gavin . . .'

'Of course I do!' she interrupted fiercely.

'. . . you'll come back to London with us and help me talk to your father,' Brodie finished as coolly as if she hadn't spoken. 'He had another mild heart attack a few months back, he isn't the man he used to be. I try not to

upset him or get into arguments with him. This
business with Gavin is going to be a big shock to him. I
want to make it as easy on him as I can—that's where
you can help.' He paused and eyed her without
expression. What was he thinking about? she wondered with a sharp stab of apprehension. She didn't like
that look in his eyes—whenever Brodie looked as calm
as a millpond you knew he was up to something. He
was a born pokerplayer, but that very blankness told
you a little—it warned you that behind his cool face he
was thinking and whatever he was planning was likely
to be potentially lethal.

'I still don't think that he'd listen to me!' But Donna
knew her voice betrayed uncertainty and of course he
heard it.

'I think you ought to go home soon anyway,' he told
her. 'Your father may not have much longer to live.'

Her breath caught and she fixed shaken eyes on him.
'Gavin didn't tell me he was that ill.'

'Gavin probably doesn't know. Your father refuses
to admit how ill he is—he's good at refusing to face
things he finds unpleasant, as I said.'

'Then what makes you think . . .'

'His doctor warned me after the last attack.'

'And you kept it to yourself? Why didn't you tell
Gavin?'

'I didn't think he could handle it.'

The cool answer took her breath away. She stared at
him dumbly, realising that he was probably right. How
would Gavin react to news like that? With shock and
distress, yes, but wouldn't he run away from facing it?

'You had no right to take that decision,' she said in a
husky voice. 'You should have let me know and I'd

have talked to Gavin.'

His brows shot up, derision in his smile. 'We weren't exactly on confidential terms,' he drawled, and watched her flush, with apparent mockery.

'I had a right to know that my father was seriously ill. What I think of you has nothing to do with it. You should have written to me.'

'It occurred to me, but I had a feeling that if you recognised my handwriting you'd file my letter in the wastepaper basket.'

'Rung me, then,' she said, beginning to lose her temper.

'Wouldn't you have hung up when you recognised my voice?'

'Oh, don't be ridiculous!' she snapped, glaring at him. 'You know you should have let me know my father might die at any minute.'

'If I'd thought it was likely to happen I'd have sent for you,' said Brodie with the cool arrogance which made her blood boil.

'Who the hell do you think you are?' she erupted. 'You'd have sent for me? As if I were an office boy? To come when you snap your fingers?'

'Make up your mind,' Brodie said drily. 'First you're angry because I didn't send for you, and then you're angry because I say I would have done if the need arose. I get it in the neck whatever I do, it seems.'

'I don't like the way you feel free to take charge of my family's affairs without consulting any of us!' she snapped.

'I'm consulting you now,' he pointed out. 'So what are you going to do about Gavin? Are you coming back to London with us or do you want me to deal with it?'

His smile held amusement. He knew she wouldn't leave it to him, after what she had just said about resenting his interference!

'I'll come back to London,' she said reluctantly. 'But I have to make arrangements first—my boss will need a warning, I can't leave until Monday, at the earliest.'

He shrugged. 'That suits me. A weekend in Paris is always a pleasure.' He glanced at his watch and got up. 'I managed to book a room at the Ritz, I'd better go and check in—I sent my luggage on with the taxi driver.'

'You may never see it again!'

'Oh, it was only a small suitcase. I brought very little with me, and in any case, I took his number.'

He moved to the door and as they walked into the corridor Gavin's face appeared at the kitchen door.

'Have dinner with me,' Brodie said casually, sharing the invitation between them.

Gavin made a horrified face and didn't answer. Donna gave him a hesitant glance, then decided it might be wiser to accept. They were going to need Brodie's help if they were going to persuade their father to recognise Gavin's deep-seated problem.

'Thank you, what time?' she said, conscious that her brother was looking furious but not daring to say anything.

'At the Ritz at seven-thirty?'

'The Ritz?' muttered Gavin, a sneer curling his mouth. 'Nice to be able to afford it. I can't, but then I don't sign my own expenses.'

Brodie gave him a sardonic glance but didn't make the obvious rejoinder.

Donna said hurriedly, 'We'll be there,' She had never been to the Ritz for dinner, but she had once had cocktails in the bar with some friends. Brodie nodded and left.

As the door shut, Gavin burst out, 'I'm not having dinner with him—it would stick in my throat. What were you talking about in there all that time? What did he say about me? What's he going to do?'

'He was telling me that Father's really very ill.'

'I told you that.'

'Brodie seems to think his condition might be more serious than we thought,' she said carefully. 'He said I ought to come back to London.'

Gavin's face brightened. 'Are you going to? Oh, Donna, please do! You can talk to Father, you always got on better with him than I did!' He gave a half-angry, half-miserable grimace.

Gavin was insecure; he had a vulnerable personality, brittle, always under threat from pressures inside himself as much as the more obvious external pressures. Gavin had learnt to despise himself and the weakness of his personal identity made him permanently angry, put him permanently at risk.

I shouldn't have left London, thought Donna. I shouldn't have left Gavin there alone. It was selfish of me to run like that, but at the time it seemed the only thing to do.

Her own sense of self had suffered a crisis two years before. Finding out that the man you're in love with is only interested in you because he wants your family company is a shattering blow. She had had to get away to grow new scar tissue over that wound. She had forgotten Gavin, and now she blamed herself. If she had been around he might never have started gambling again.

'When will you come?' asked Gavin, as she sat down at the breakfast table with a fresh pot of coffee ten minutes later.

'On Monday. I have to talk to my boss first—I'll try to ring him at home this weekend, but he may have gone to the country. They have a cottage near Chartres and try to get there as often as possible.' She poured herself some coffee and took a croissant. Brodie's arrival had wrecked her appetite. She ate very little breakfast before going to shower and get dressed.

Gavin was just going out again when she saw him half an hour later. 'I thought I'd buy a paper and walk down to the river, have a coffee at a pavement café near Notre Dame,' he told her.

He was already more cheerful now that his problem was half solved. She smiled at him wryly. 'What about lunch? Shall I meet you somewhere?'

They arranged to meet outside Notre Dame at half past twelve and have lunch in the Latin Quarter at one of the cheap bistros. When he had gone Donna rang her boss and was lucky enough to catch him just as he was about to leave for Chartres. He was sympathetic when he heard her news and gave her a week off to visit her father. It wasn't difficult for her to arrange time off because she worked as a translator for a big inter-national magazine and did most of her work at home, translating English articles into French. Her editor would simply transfer her workload to another trans-lator. He had whole strings of them working for him part-time—it was an easy way for a student to earn spare cash. Donna was fully employed by the magazine and earned a considerable amount more than she had when she first arrived in Paris. If she worked long hours she could earn very well indeed, and she enjoyed the work. She knew that the magazine liked the way she translated articles; she could echo style in a way that the more pedestrian translators never did. It was a knack which had improved with practice, and she also worked part-time for other firms—several publishers gave her work and if they had nothing for her she translated letters for a multi-national company, but she rarely had to fall back on that as a source of income these days. She was too well established in the publishing world.

She spent an hour making sure that her apartment was tidy and then did some quick shopping in the neighbourhood before taking the Metro to Notre Dame. She found Gavin basking in the sun among a crowd of tourists watching a white-faced mime artist. Donna sat with her brother for a while to catch some of the act, then they dropped a few francs into the top-hat laid on the ground and strolled away to find somewhere to eat.

The Latin Quarter of Paris is well supplied with bistros of all sorts; mainly foreign—Greek, Turkish, Algerian. Gavin decided he felt like some Algerian food, so they went in to eat cous-cous followed by a sticky sweetmeat made with nuts and sesame seeds, liberally laced with honey.

'I don't know why you don't live nearer the centre of things,' Gavin commented as they wandered along the river in the afternoon sunshine. 'You're so far from anywhere in that apartment.'

Donna gave him a wry sideways look. 'That's what I like about the apartment. It's peaceful.'

He wrinkled his nose. 'Dull, you mean.'

'You and I have very different tastes!'

He was serious suddenly. 'I wish you hadn't left London, Donna. Things were better while you were there.'

She slid her hand through his arm, leaning on him. 'Don't be glum. We'll sort this out—but you must stop gambling, Gavin.'

'I will,' he said with emphasis, but he had promised that once before and broken his word.

They took a taxi back to her apartment an hour later. Gavin was sleepy after being out in the sun for some hours, and kept yawning.

'I haven't slept too well for two nights now.' He gave her a furtive look which she noticed. 'Donna, I'm not having dinner with Brodie Fox. I can't—the food would choke me. I don't know how you can be polite to the man. He's our enemy, don't you realise that?'

Her smile was grim. 'Oh, I realise it, but sometimes you have to have a truce, even with someone you don't trust an inch. You're going to need his help with Father, you'd better face that. He could do you irreparable harm if you offend him, and he wouldn't hesitate to do it, either. Having dinner with him is the least of our worries. Compared to what Father is going to say when he knows about the money, a dinner with Brodie Fox will be a picnic!'

Gavin did not appear to be any more cheerful about the prospect. As they let themselves into the apartment, he said wearily, 'Couldn't you go alone and let me try to catch up on my sleep?'

She eyed him ruefully. 'Don't be such a coward, Gavin!' But what was the use of saying that? Gavin's reluctance to face anything unpleasant was one of the problems she had to sort out.

His eyes pleaded and she sighed. 'Oh, very well. Go to bed then and I'll see Brodie on my own.'

'Dinner at the Ritz should be quite a sugar-coating for the pill,' said Gavin, immediately lighthearted again.

Donna didn't bother to answer that—just watched him saunter off to bed, her expression ironic. Gavin had no idea how hard it was going to be for her to stay cool and pretend to enjoy the food, however fantastic, while Brodie sat opposite her.

Gavin was almost entirely self-centred. He simply failed to notice what was happening to other people; their feelings passed him by, he didn't suspect what they were thinking. His private myopia had some advantages. He hadn't noticed two years ago that she was wildly in love with Brodie Fox. He knew, of course, that their father had wanted her to marry Brodie—like Gavin, their father was blithely ruthless about getting what he wanted. He had made his views crystal clear and expected her to fall into line. Gavin had sympathised and urged her to defy James Cowley, but the complexities of the situation had escaped him. He had no idea how hard it was for her to refuse and go away rather than put up with their father's bullying, and she hadn't bothered to enlighten him.

She changed into an austere black cocktail dress, knowing full well that she was going to find the Ritz crammed with elegant Frenchwomen. Her dress wasn't expensive, but it had the chic of utter simplicity and had been made by a friend of Marie-Louise who was studying *haute couture* in Paris. Most of Donna's friends were also Marie-Louise's; Donna had met them through Marie-Louise, who had been a nurse in a private clinic in Paris. Through her job, she had met a good many famous and influential people, a few of whom had become her friends, and through her had become Donna's friends too.

She had met Marie-Louise in a dentist's waiting-room shortly after she came to Paris. They had had to wait for ages while the dentist attended to an abscess on someone's tooth, and had begun to talk because it took their minds off their own nerves. They might never have met again if fate hadn't taken a hand. The very next day they walked into each other outside Galeries Lafayette and at once stopped, smiling. They had coffee together and from then on they were friends. Perhaps if she hadn't met the other girl, Donna might never have settled down so happily in Paris. Marie-Louise had a wide circle of friends and a busy social life into which Donna fitted easily. Having come to Paris to train as a nurse to be near her fiancé who had been working in a Paris hospital, Marie-Louise had stayed on after he got a job back in Lyons because she could earn so much more in the clinic and they needed as much as possible to start their married life. Every so often she would fly home to Lyons and occasionally Jean-Paul flew to Paris to meet her. They were both very disciplined, which had misled Donna into thinking Marie-Louise wasn't really in love, but she had realised she was wrong in time.

There was no sound from Gavin's room as she let herself out of the apartment. He must have gone to sleep immediately. Her face wry, she thought that it was just as well. He would make an uncomfortable third that evening. Brodie didn't hide his impatience with him and Gavin resented Brodie's strength.

She took a taxi to the Place Vendôme where Napoleon's column brooded over the pale canopies of the Hotel Ritz, a favourite spot for Parisian society to dine on summer evenings in a garden haunted with pale pink sphinxes. The desk clerk told her that she would find Brodie in the bar on the left; he had walked that way a moment ago.

Turning into the bar, Donna found it full of people. A pianist was playing Cole Porter by the window, which stood open, a warm breeze bringing the fragrance of geraniums into the slightly stuffy room. Donna hovered, looking around, but couldn't see Brodie at any of the tables.

Someone saw her, however, and stood up, waving. 'Donna! *Ça va, chérie?*'

'Alain! *Comment allez-vous?*' She went over to his table, smiling in surprise. Alain Roche was a small, dark, rather ugly little man with faintly bulging eyes which had given him the nickname *la Grenouille*. He was a journalist on a satirical newspaper run by the Left in Paris and had enormous charm which made him apparently quite irresistible to women, who fell for him in such vast numbers that his friends called them *les mouches*. Alain's flies buzzed everywhere he went. His friends said he gobbled them up, but in fact they rarely lost touch with him, even after an affair was over. Alain's lady friends became just friends once passion had burnt out. Donna had never been one of them, but she was fond of Alain who was very witty and sophisticated, a charming companion, and he, in his turn, seemed to like her, perhaps because he found his sexual reputation trying, to live up to, and was grateful that with one woman, at least, he did not have to play the conqueror.

He asked what she was doing at the Ritz, made a mock grimace at hearing that she was there to have dinner with another man, and invited her to have a drink, but, aware of the far-from-cordial gaze of the woman sitting next to him, she smilingly excused herself and left the bar again, in search of Brodie.

Alain followed her a moment later and caught up with her. *'Au secours, chérie! C'est une peste! J'aimerais mieux être avec toi!'*

She laughed. 'Poor woman, what's wrong with her?' she asked in French.

He told her in his hoarse, rapid French that the other woman was a shrew; jealous, demanding, exhausting. *'Je vais devenir un ennemi des femmes!'* he announced to her amusement.

'Bravo!' she said gravely, kissing him on both cheeks. The idea of Alain as a woman-hater was so absurd it was hard to keep a straight face.

Alain returned the formal salute, assumed a suffering expression and went back into the bar. It was only then that Donna realised that they had an audience. Brodie was standing a few feet away, radiating brooding displeasure.

'Where did you find that weird-looking character?' he asked curtly, moving towards her. 'Is he a sample of the sort of men you've been dating while you've been here? I can't say I admire your taste. No amount of kisses would turn him into a fairy prince.'

CHAPTER THREE

THEY had dinner in the famous garden behind high walls, the sound of music floating out from the bar at one end and the chatter of French voices from the dining-room to one side of their table. Among the flowerbeds lurked the pink sphinxes carved with the Pompadour's face. Moths were just beginning to flit around the candles lighted on each table. The sky had an almost purple bloom pricked with sharp white stars. It should have been a magical, romantic occasion. It was more like a duel to the death.

'Alain is a friend,' Donna had told him an hour earlier in the foyer outside the bar, and Brodie had been asking ever since about her life in Paris over the last two years. Donna told him as little as she could; she resented his questions, and felt that every scrap of information she gave him might some time, somehow, be used against her.

'So there's nobody special in your life?' he asked, watching her with eyes that gleamed like blue fire in the candlelight.

'I didn't say that.'

'You don't say much at all, do you?'

She gave him a tight little smile. 'Why should I? You keep asking me about my private life—you don't tell me anything about yours.'

'You haven't asked.' He gave her a curling, inviting smile which she met stonily.

45

'I'm not interested.'

He didn't like that. The hooded lids lowered and his smile smoothed out, the pared planes of his face taut again. Donna put out a hand to her glass; relieved to see that her fingers were steady. Brodie's repressed anger had made her nervous, but luckily it didn't show.

They had both had cheese soufflé, light as air; melting on their tongues. The wine had a smoky tang which matched it perfectly. It had irritated her that Brodie hadn't asked what she wanted to drink. During her two years in Paris she had learnt a great deal about French wine and enjoyed choosing what to drink with food. She had to admit, though, that he had picked the right wine for the soufflé. She didn't tell him so; she was giving nothing away tonight.

'Gavin couldn't face dinner, I gather?' he enquired.

'He couldn't face your company, would be more accurate,' she said frankly.

His eyes were ironic. 'He resents me,' he agreed. 'Not very logical of him, but then I suppose one can't expect logic from someone as screwed up as Gavin.'

'Why should it be illogical for him to resent you?' she asked sweetly. 'Doesn't everybody?'

The waiter removed their plates. When he had gone Brodie leaned forward and said, 'You and Gavin aren't everybody.'

The wine waiter appeared and poured red wine into their second glass with the sort of reverent expression that made Donna want to giggle. Wine buffs were okay so long as they didn't take themselves or their wines too seriously, she had learnt. Wine was to be enjoyed, not treated as a holy sacrament.

When they were alone again, she smiled coldly at

Brodie. 'My father thinks you're the cat's whiskers, I'm aware of that.'

'And that's why Gavin resents me? If I hadn't joined the firm, does he think his father would think any more highly of him? I'm not in competition with Gavin, even if he imagines he's in competition with me. I do my job as well as I know how . . .'

'And you're ambitious,' Donna said curtly.

'What's wrong with that? You think ambition is some sort of unmentionable disease?'

'It depends how you pursue it.'

'Now what are you implying? That I'm not honest?'

She laughed angrily. 'Oh, I'm sure you're far too clever to make the mistake of being dishonest. You're not human enough to make mistakes.'

'Not human enough?' he repeated, his jawline taut. 'What the hell does that mean? You admire Gavin's brand of humanity more, I suppose? If I had a few more weaknesses you'd like me better. What do you want me to do—embezzle money, drink, start taking cocaine?'

'Don't be absurd, that wasn't what I meant, and you know it!'

'Then what did you mean? You prefer your men to be weak so that you can get them on their knees?'

The waiter reappeared looking professionally blank, but Donna saw his quick, curious glance at her and knew that he had not only overheard Brodie's last remark but had understood it. She felt herself flush and clenched her teeth with rage. At least she didn't have to reply to that while they were being served with their next course, but she brooded over it while she sipped the red wine and toyed with her food. It was a pity that the meal had been eaten in a tense atmosphere, because

the cuisine here was superb. She had always wanted to
eat at the Ritz; all her friends said it was fabulous. She
couldn't wait to tell them they were absolutely right.
There were no prices on the menu, and she shuddered
to think how much all this was costing. Of course she
wasn't paying, but she couldn't help wondering if her
father approved of Brodie living like a king on
company expenses.

Through lowered lashes she assessed his elegant dark
suit; his clothes were obviously very expensive. He
sneered at Gavin for embezzling money from the
firm—but how on earth did he get her father to approve
of the way *he* spent money? He had said that he didn't
bother her father with the day-to-day running of the
company, hadn't he? Did that mean that her father no
longer checked up on him? Was Brodie quite as
incorruptible as she had imagined? Was he quite as
faultless?

While they were being served with their coffee Alain
and his companion came through the french windows
to have dinner in the garden. The woman noticed
Donna, gave her a frosty stare, but swept past. Alain
lingered, asking in French how Donna had enjoyed her
meal.

'Marvellous,' she said, smiling, in the same language.
'Try the *foie gras frais*, it's out of this world.' She
wondered how good Brodie's French was—did he
understand what they were saying? She had noticed
that he understood the menu without needing help, but
he had spoken English to the waiters. Perhaps he was
sensitive about his accent? After two years, hers was no
longer so obviously foreign, but she had been through a
phase of feeling self-conscious about it.

Alain gave Brodie several brief glances, so Donna politely introduced them. Brodie smiled coldly, inclined his head. Alain looked amused. He was used to getting hostility from other men. His reputation made them wary, especially if they had wives.

Ignoring the smouldering looks he was getting from his own table Alain asked quickly, 'Will you be coming to the party tomorrow?'

'Olga's party! Oh, I'd forgotten—no, I'm afraid I can't make it, I'm leaving for London on Monday.'

Alain pulled a droll face. *'C'est affreux! Est-ce tu pars longtemps?'*

She shook her head, aware of Brodie watching her closely. 'No, I doubt if I'll be there long—and I'll be coming to Lyons as arranged, so I'll see you then.'

Alain gazed into her eyes, smiling wickedly. He was as conscious of Brodie's icy attention as she was and deliberately played to the gallery, taking her hand and kissing it lingeringly.

'I look forward to our weekend together more than I can say,' he murmured. *'Au revoir, chérie—jusqu'alors.'*

He sauntered away, and she glanced at Brodie with hidden apprehension, trying not to smile.

Brodie called for the bill with a peremptory wave of his hand. It wasn't until they were outside the hotel and the doorman was getting Donna a taxi that Brodie asked crisply, 'You're going away for the weekend with that Frenchman?'

Donna turned innocent eyes on him, nodding. 'Next weekend, to be precise.'

'You'd better cancel it. You won't be going,' said Brodie, biting out the words like someone snapping cotton with their teeth.

'Oh, yes, I will,' Donna said firmly. The taxi drew up and the doorman opened the door for her. She began to get in and Brodie leaned forward, his face dark.

'You'll still be in London next weekend.'

'Thank you for the wonderful meal,' she said, her tones melting. 'Goodnight.'

He stood back, the door was closed and the taxi moved away. Donna leaned back, closing her eyes. She hoped he wasn't going back into the restaurant to have a vicious confrontation with poor Alain, although if he did, Alain would have brought it on himself because he hadn't been able to resist showing off. He'd deliberately given Brodie the wrong impression because it amused him. He must have been very curious when he saw her dining alone at the Ritz with Brodie. Donna usually went around with a crowd of friends. She didn't have a boy-friend. She had had plenty of offers and had gone out with a few people briefly, but none of them had been what she was looking for; they didn't measure up to her memories of Brodie. She couldn't take any of them seriously, and there was safety in numbers.

Many times during the past two years she had been angry with herself because after Brodie all other men seemed shadowy. He hadn't been what she thought he was; it had all been an illusion, a clever conjuring trick performed by an ambitious man who knew precisely what he was doing. She hated him but she couldn't forget him and she couldn't fall in love with anyone else, however hard she tried.

The next day she and Gavin had lunch in a small family restaurant on the Quai Voltaire across the river from the Louvre. It was a café-tabac, simple and unpretentious, with tables out on the pavement. They ate Risotto de Homard and drank Sancerre, watching the people flocking along by the river, crossing the Pont du Carrousel. The food was good and inexpensive for what it was.

'Voltaire died in one of the rooms up there,' Donna told her brother, pointing upwards.

'I think I'd like to live in Paris,' said Gavin, showing no interest in the great French writer whatever. 'I like the pace of life here.'

'Oh, but it's August,' Donna said. 'Paris is a different place in August—come back in November and see how you like it then!'

'You obviously like it,' her brother pointed out.

'I love it,' she agreed, laughing. 'But I work here, my life's here. When you're on holiday, there's no hassle. Try getting the Metro late at night or try catching a taxi during the rush-hour, in the rain. When you live somewhere all the time you see it differently.'

They walked back to her apartment slowly, stopping several times to have a glass of mineral water or a coffee at pavement cafés en route, so that it took them a long time. Gavin loved to sit in a café watching the flow of people, the rustling leaves of the chestnut trees, the rush of traffic. The drawn look had been smoothed out of his face and his smile was brighter. He would have been much happier if he hadn't had to please their father all his life. Gavin couldn't take any sort of pressure; he was too weak.

'Have you got a girl at the moment?' she asked him lightly.

He gave her a wry grin. 'Dozens.'

'I meant one you were serious about!'

'I know you did. No, not really. What about you?'

Her face sobered. She shook her head.

'Do you think we're too hard to please?' he murmured with a rueful expression. 'Do you want to get married, Donna? I don't, I couldn't take the responsibility—just thinking about it makes me shudder. Mortgages, insurance policies, being tied down to one woman and having kids—no, not me!'

'It's a pity you don't like working in the firm, though,' she said, sighing. 'Is it the work itself you hate, or . . .'

'I stifle shut up in an office all day,' Gavin said sulkily. 'I sit at my desk and dictate letters to this boring woman who's supposed to be my secretary and sometimes I can hardly keep my eyes open. Brodie Fox picked her out for me. You should see her! I think she takes steroids; she has muscles like an all-in wrestler, and a little moustache. I keep waiting for her to grow a beard. She marches into my office with her pad and barks at me like a drill sergeant, and I'm too scared of her to tell her to go away and leave me alone.'

She laughed. 'Poor woman—I don't envy her.' She glanced at him uncertainly. 'Maybe if you took more interest in the glass production you'd enjoy work more.'

Gavin laughed shortly. 'You mean start working at the factory? That's probably where I'm going to end up—when Brodie Fox is in charge he'll put me on a stool beside the conveyor belt watching for flaws.' A flicker of laughter went through his face. 'When I was a kid I remember I used to want to be the guy who took a hammer to the rejects and fed them back into the process to be re-cycled. There's something rather satisfying about smashing glass, don't you think?'

Their company was one of the biggest manufacturers

of industrial glass in Britain. They had several factories; one in the Midlands and another in the North and a third near London in one of the new towns built since the Second World War. The company head-quarters in London co-ordinated the running of all three. They had offices in a large building a stone's throw from St Paul's Cathedral, in a new modern office complex. Until six years ago the firm had been entirely family owned, but then their father had decided to go public in order to raise more capital with which to finance an expansion programme. That was when they had taken over the factory site in the new town. Fifty one per cent of the shares had been retained in James Cowley's hands so that he hadn't lost control of the firm, and his gamble had paid off—the stock was more valuable today than it had been when it was first launched and they were paying a good dividend.

Donna looked thoughtfully at her brother. 'I wonder if you shouldn't have started at the factory long ago? You liked making things, didn't you? All those model kits, remember?'

Gavin grimaced. 'Not the same thing. That was fun. Making moulded glass is work and even today the factory's hardly a comfortable work place. The sort of glass I might have liked to make is . . .' He broke off, shrugging. 'Oh well, what does it matter?'

'Of course it matters! What were you going to say?' she asked as they went into the apartment building.

Madame Lebrun and her husband were behind their lace curtains, eating a late lunch. Donna recognised the smell of *soupe de poissons*—rich, aromatic, heavily spiced. Madame often made it; throwing all sorts of cheap fish into a pot with herbs and spices and tomatoes, letting it cook for hours so that the smell permeated the whole house.

They didn't stop eating, but they watched Donna and her brother walk past, their eyes unblinkingly curious. 'What on earth are they eating?' muttered Gavin. 'Extraordinary smell.'

'Fish stew.'

'Fish? It smells like curry.'

'That's the spices. I think Madame uses lots of spice to hide the fact that she buys the cheapest fish.'

Gavin paused, panting. 'My God, how do you put up with all these stairs every time you go in and out? Why do you live right at the top of the house?'

'It's cheaper than the lower floors and the view is better. It's quieter at night, too,' Donna told him.

'You're so damned practical,' he muttered.

When they were in the kitchen of her apartment drinking some tea, she asked him, 'What were you going to say as we got here? Something about the sort of glass you would have liked to make?'

'Oh, it was just a stupid idea I used to have when I was a kid—I always thought I'd rather like to blow glass. Not work on the factory line, I hate the automated production process we use in the factories. I used to daydream about actually making glass the way they used to in the days before automation. There's something so magical about blowing glass by hand; shaping it, making it do what you want. It's a bit like blowing bubbles; watching them grow, all shimmery, like rainbows, then float away. Sheer magic!'

'Did you ever tell Father that you wanted to blow glass by hand?'

Gavin gave her an angry smile. 'Oh, I was crazy

enough to mention it when I was about fourteen, I remember.'

'What did he say?'

'That I was joking. When I said I was serious he told me to grow up, he said there was nothing in making glass by hand, it was a game for amateurs. He said I had to learn to run the company and wasn't to waste my time daydreaming. So I gave up the idea.'

Donna looked at him grimly. 'Just like that?'

'What was I supposed to do? Argue with him? You know what he's like. He doesn't really listen. He just waits for you to see it his way and if you don't he gets very nasty.' Gavin pushed his cup away, his mouth sulky. 'And, anyway, I doubt if I'd have been very good at glass-blowing. I would only have wasted a few years trying to pick up the techniques and then had to crawl back to Father with my tail between my legs.'

'Oh Gavin, don't be so defeatist!'

'I'm not defeatist, I'm just realistic.'

The phone began to ring and Donna sighed, getting up. 'Sometimes I think you need a good shake.'

'I get one every day of my life.' Gavin said, and laughed. Donna didn't think it was so funny.

It was Brodie on the phone, sounding oddly far away. 'We'll be flying tomorrow at ten,' he said. 'Where have you been all day?'

'Showing Gavin around Paris.'

'Show it to me tonight. We could walk along the river—there's a glorious moon.'

His husky voice made her see stars. She swallowed. 'If we're leaving early tomorrow I'd better get an early night.'

'Coward,' he said softly, but he didn't try to talk her

into going. As she put down the phone a few minutes later she crossly admitted to herself that she had half hoped he would. He might at least have tried. It was a gorgeous night and she could see the moon above the Paris skyline, mysterious and glimmering; it must look terrific on the Seine. They might have taken a trip on the Bateau Mouche, floating on the silvery waters, under the bridges, silently, romantically. Donna shrugged, laughing at her own imagery. It sounded fabulous, but she had taken those trips, she knew that there would be children running about yelling and wanting to go to the toilet, a nasal Tannoy telling you about the famous buildings on each bank, people eating and drinking all around you.

That didn't mean it would have been wise or safe to go. Brodie was a lethal combination with anything, however unromantic. He would have been there, those blue eyes inviting, mocking. She would have had difficulty staying cool. No, much better to turn him down and stay in tonight. Tomorrow was going to be a trying day. Tomorrow she was going to see her father for the first time in two years.

Brodie picked them up from the apartment next morning in a taxi and they all drove to the airport together in the usual heavy traffic. It was the rush-hour both ways—people driving into Paris to work, people driving out of Paris to get to Charles de Gaulle airport. Their taxi driver made frustrated, Gallic noises as he tried to make his way through other traffic. Gavin chewed his fingernails and ignored Brodie. Brodie stayed calm as a cucumber and Donna wished she wasn't so aware of being sandwiched between him and

Gavin; Brodie's knee touching hers, his arm laid along the back of the seat, ostensibly to make room for her. She kept feeling his fingers. They didn't quite touch her, but they were there, almost against the nape of her neck, softly drumming on the back of the seat. They drove her crazy.

She was glad when they finally got to the airport and were sucked into the usual formula of checking in, going through passport control, hanging around waiting to board. She hurried into the duty-free shops to buy some perfume, bought herself some magazines to read on the plane and had a cup of coffee. Brodie and Gavin sat in the café in silence. Brodie read his morning paper. Gavin stared at nothing. This morning he was very sullen. He was going home under escort, like a naughty boy who had run away from school. He wasn't looking forward to his reception, even though Donna would be there to act as a buffer against the worst of their father's anger.

As they arrived in London it was raining. 'Home, sweet home,' Donna said bitterly, following her brother down the steps of the plane. 'Wouldn't you know it?'

'Laid on just for us,' Gavin said glumly. His gloom infected her. She felt deeply depressed at the thought of being back in London, returning to her father and the home she had thought she had left for ever. Throughout her childhood nothing had ever seemed to change in James Cowley's house, any more than it had in him. From all that Gavin had told her, that still applied— and yet from Brodie she had picked up a very different picture. He seemed to think her father was a changed man; a very ill man who was slowly winding down.

Of course, Brodie and Gavin saw it from sharply

separated angles. Brodie merely worked for James
Cowley. Gavin was subject to his father in many other
ways—not least the emotional slavery of being a highly
unsatisfactory son.

A loved and happy child has an emotional security
which means the freedom to come or go, knowing that
either way it is still loved. Gavin was neither free nor
secure because he felt he wasn't loved.

Her father didn't feel much for either of them. He
had been silent ever since she went away. At times she
had wondered if he had really noticed that she wasn't
there.

Well, he was going to notice her return, because she
was going to tell him what he had done to Gavin, what
he was still doing to him.

Brodie's car was parked in the car park at Heathrow,
and within a few minutes of landing they were driving
north-east, making for James Cowley's home near
Saffron Walden. He had a flat in town, too, so that he
didn't have to make the long trip out into Essex late at
night on the occasions when he had a dinner to attend,
but since he had retired no doubt he had given up the
flat, Donna thought.

Brodie drove and she sat beside him in the front seat,
watching as London suburbs gave way to familiar
countryside. Two years away hadn't altered much.

As they got deeper into the countryside it stopped
raining and a rainbow broke; watery, shimmering, a
blue sky behind it. The fields were full of ripe, golden
wheat and barley just being harvested; they passed
several machines trundling back and forth behind the
berried hedges. Black wings flapped above the tumbling barley; crows following the harvester and

watching for disturbed mice and perhaps a baby rabbit. Donna frowned, looking away. She didn't like crows. Ominous birds.

She glanced over her shoulder at her brother who was also staring out of the window. Gavin was wrapped in thought; not very happy thought, from his drawn face.

'How does it feel to be back?' asked Brodie, abruptly.

She started, looking at him. 'Odd. Like going to the dentist.'

'You'll feel better once it's over,' he deduced, a wry smile curving his mouth.

'Does my father know we're coming?'

'No, I decided not to tell him anything in case I didn't get Gavin back here.'

'You thought he might bolt again before we arrived?'

'It occurred to me.'

It had occurred to her, too, and she was relieved that her brother hadn't slipped off before they got into the car.

'That's really why you insisted that I came, wasn't it?' she said, watching his profile. It had a carved authority in the afternoon light. He wasn't smiling; he could have been a statue.

'One reason,' he admitted drily. 'I thought it might make sure Gavin actually went home.'

'What were the other reasons?'

His eyes slid sideways, a glint in them. 'I'll tell you when we're alone.'

Her nerves jumped. What did he mean by that? 'I can't stay long.' she said hurriedly. 'I have to be in Lyons next weekend, remember.'

Brodie's face changed, the smile going, a harsh frown taking its place. 'You can't be serious!' His voice was curt. 'I don't believe you're having an affair with that little creep.'

'I didn't say I was—yet,' said Donna, finding it ridiculously hard to lie to him.

He shot her a hard look. 'And you're not going to!'

The peremptory tone made her bristle. 'That's my decision, not yours.'

'We'll see about that,' he muttered, turning into the drive of her father's house. She hadn't even noticed that they were almost there, she had been too absorbed in arguing with Brodie.

'You'll mind your own business,' she told him through her teeth, staring at the house ahead of them. It was a simple late Georgian house with a classic façade: flat windows, a columned portico, the local pargeting on the stucco covering the bricks, in a pattern of curved lines.

'I'm not letting you go,' Brodie said, and hot colour stung her face.

'*You're* not letting me go? I don't remember asking for your permission—it's nothing to do with you who I sleep with.'

He pulled up outside the house with a screech of tyres on gravel and swung round towards her, rage in his face. She had never seen him that angry before; she had never seen the usual calm of his face broken by such violence. It made her flinch, as if she thought he was going to hit her.

Then he turned away and got out of the car, slamming the door with a thud that made the glass in the windows rattle.

Gavin whistled. 'Hey, what's up with him?'

She looked round and her brother was very pale;

trying to smile, to hide his nerves.

'Come on, Gavin, let's go in together,' she said, smiling at him. 'Father doesn't know anything yet, Brodie says—so let me tell him later. Don't you say anything to him.'

Gavin groaned. 'I couldn't if I tried. I've been sitting here all the way from Heathrow, wondering what to say.'

'Just leave it to me,' soothed Donna. She was afraid that even at this late stage, Gavin might bolt for it.

Brodie was under the portico, ringing the front doorbell. By the time Gavin and Donna joined him, the door was opening. Their father's housekeeper, Mrs Eyre, looked incredulously at Donna.

'Good heavens!' she exclaimed.

'Hallo, Mrs Eyre. How are you?'

'Well, I never,' the woman babbled, laughing. 'Oh, I'm fine, your father didn't tell me you were coming, Donna—he must be getting absent-minded. Don't you look brown? No need to ask how you are. I can see. I'd say your hair's fairer than it used to be too; bleached by the sun, I suppose. I've never been to France. Is it very hot there? Good heavens, this is ... well, I'm speechless. It's been such a long time. You've changed, yes, you have. But it's lovely to see you again. Come in, come in, we mustn't stand here all day, your father will be wanting to see you.'

Donna wasn't so sure about that. Brodie had just brought the cases from the car; his ironic eyes met hers as she glanced away from the housekeeper's excited face.

Attracted by the commotion in the hall, James Cowley suddenly came out of his study at the far end, pulling his glasses off, his eyes irritated.

'Really, Mrs Eyre! What is all the noise? You know I can't work with . . .' His voice broke off as he recognised his daughter. 'Donna?' he whispered, as if unable to believe his eyes.

She hadn't expected to be so overthrown by seeing him. He looked older than she had remembered, older than she had feared. His hair had gone quite white, his face was thin and lined, and he looked ill. She could see the etching of pain on his face and winced. The neck rising out of his collar was hollowed, wrinkled, grey; his eyes had sunk deep into his head. If she had seen him from a distance she might not have known him.

'Hallo, Father,' she said huskily, going towards him to kiss him.

'You've come home?' he asked in a shaky voice as her lips brushed his face. His eyes were glistening; Donna had never known him to show emotion before, not to her. Brodie hadn't been lying to her—her father wasn't the same man. The change was deep-seated; his personality had been wrenched into other paths by the approach of death. Brodie was right—her father hadn't long to live. She couldn't speak, biting her lip and blinking back tears she was ashamed to shed, feeling an emotion she had not been taught to express. All her life her father had been a cold distant figure in the background. She didn't know how to respond to this stranger; involuntarily her eyes moved to Brodie, asking him to help her.

'I brought her back from Paris,' he said, reading the plea in her face as he put down the cases on the carpet.

James Cowley looked at him, his eyes widening. 'You brought her back?' There was an odd, excited note in his voice, he began to smile and threw an arm around his daughter, hugging her awkwardly. It was the first time in many years that he had spontaneously shown her affection and he was self-conscious, very aware of it.

'My dear girl, this is wonderful news! Brodie, you've been very secretive, but never mind—I can't tell you how glad I am to see you two together again!'

Donna stiffened as she realised he was jumping to conclusions from what Brodie had said. She looked angrily at Brodie; eyes commanding him to tell her father he was wrong, to say or do something, not just stand there looking amused.

'When will . . .' James Cowley began, and suddenly broke off, gasping for breath, his hands clutching at his chest. Donna saw him sag at the knees and caught hold of him instinctively, going white.

'Father? What is it?'

Brodie got there before the older man fell to the floor. It was Brodie who caught his waist and lifted him over his shoulder, carrying him easily into the sitting-room, where he laid him down on the couch. 'Get the ambulance,' he threw over his shoulder at Mrs Eyre, who ran to the phone. 'Donna, top drawer in your father's desk, in the study—pills, run, get them. Gavin, get a glass of water, quickly, quickly, don't gape at me!'

Donna was already out of the room and into the study. She pulled open the top drawer in the desk and at once found the bottle of capsules. As she straightened she saw the photo on the desk: a studio portrait of herself, framed in silver. It had been taken when she was eleven; she had freckles across her nose and a gap between her teeth. She had totally forgotten the photograph until she saw it again.

She turned away biting her lip, and ran back to
Brodie with the pills. Had that picture been on her
father's desk for more then twelve years?

Brodie grabbed the pill bottle and shook out two
capsules into his hand, looking round. 'Hurry up,
Gavin!' he said impatiently as Gavin slowly came
through the door.

James Cowley's eyes were shut; he breathed sterto-
rously, his face grey. Donna found herself twisting her
fingers behind her back like a child making a wish.
Please God don't let him die, she thought with an
intensity that amazed her. He mustn't, he mustn't! She
stared fixedly at Brodie as he gently, deftly, lifted her
father's head and helped him take the capsules with a
swallow of water. Brodie knew what to do. He hadn't
lost his head. She hated him, but in this crisis she had
instinctively relied on him. He was that sort of man.

CHAPTER FOUR

DONNA fell asleep in the hospital waiting-room. When Brodie shook her gently she woke up, bewildered, staring at him with wide startled eyes. She had forgotten what had happened, where she was, for a few seconds. Then she remembered, and the flush of sleep ran out of her face.

'Is he . . .?'

'Sleeping,' Brodie told her quickly. 'He's stabilised, and the doctor's quite pleased with him.'

A sigh of relief made her shudder. She had been sitting there for hours waiting to hear how the fight for her father's life was going. She felt totally disorientated.

'There's no point in waiting, they won't let you see him,' Brodie told her. 'I'll drive you home now.'

'Home?' The word had a lost sound. He looked at her sharply.

'Come on, Donna. What you need is some breakfast and then you're going to bed. You know it's morning, or hadn't you noticed yet?'

The stark waiting-room was full of grey daylight, she realised with surprise. She hadn't noticed dawn; she must have slept through it.

'Where's Gavin?' she asked, frowning, looking around the room. Her brother had sat with her all night, but he had vanished now.

'He went for a walk to get some air half an hour ago. He said he'd get a taxi home.'

'And you let him go?' she asked angrily, immediately anxious.

'I'm not his keeper.'

'What if he runs away again?'

'With his father this ill? You don't think he'll do that, do you, Donna? I don't.' Brodie's voice was calmly assured. She wished she felt quite as sure about it. Gavin was unpredictable, especially when he was emotionally disturbed.

'He might do anything,' she muttered, following Brodie out of the waiting-room. The hospital was waking up; clangs and rattles came from all the wards, nurses walked quickly, their shoes squeaking, patients groaned to see another morning come so soon. There was a smell of hot fat from the vast kitchens on the ground floor as they made their way to the exit, and Donna's stomach protested. She was hungry and yet queasy. She didn't feel like food, although she hadn't eaten for many hours.

It was as they were driving away that she really looked at Brodie, noticing that his jaw carried a faint stubble. He hadn't shaved since yesterday morning and it was beginning to show.

'You look quite sinister,' she told him with faint malice.

He threw her a puzzled look. 'What?'

'You need a shave.'

He glanced into his driving-mirror, grimaced ruefully at what he saw and ran a hand around his chin. 'Distinctly dishevelled,' he agreed, then smiled teasingly at her. 'Have you seen yourself?'

She blinked. 'I'd rather not.'

Brodie laughed. 'Very wise. We both show signs of

wear and tear. It's been quite a night.'

She sighed and he put out a hand to her knee, patting it lightly. Donna flinched and he took his hand away, frowning.

They finished the drive back to the house in silence. Mrs Eyre opened the door to them, her face pale, eyelids red as if she had been up all night too, or had been crying.

'How is he?' she burst out.

'Comfortable,' said Brodie, smiling at her. 'Holding his own is how they put it, I think. It wasn't a major attack, thank God.'

Mrs Eyre looked at Donna. 'I'm so glad. You look very tired, you ought to go up to bed and catch up on your sleep.'

'I think we ought to have breakfast first,' said Brodie.

'No, I'm not hungry,' Donna said flatly.

'Some coffee and toast, Mrs Eyre—and a boiled egg?' Brodie ignored her protest. 'Orange juice? Fruit?'

Mrs Eyre vanished and Donna turned on him. 'I don't want any breakfast—do you really think I can eat after last night? I feel sick.'

'I think you ought to try. It will make everything feel more normal. Even if you just drink some milk and eat a slice or two of orange it would give your stomach something to do and stop you feeling as though your insides had turned to water.'

How had he known the way she felt? Donna eyed him moodily. She didn't like the way he seemed to guess what went on inside her; it made her feel exposed.

'You'll see, you'll be able to sleep after a light meal.'

Brodie pushed her into the downstairs bathroom. 'Go and wash your face and hands and come into the morning-room.'

She gave him a sulky look. 'Sure you don't want to check that I wash behind my ears?'

She didn't wait for an answer, she banged the bathroom door and ran the taps noisily. Splashing lukewarm water on her face made her wake up a little. She didn't bother to put on fresh make-up. She joined Brodie in the morning-room, her face clean and faintly flushed, her blonde hair combed and tidy.

The room was small and with early sunlight dancing across the pale green walls looked cool and yet bright. Brodie stood at the window, staring into the gardens.

Donna picked up the morning paper on the table and glanced without much interest at the headlines. Nothing much seemed to matter this morning. She felt a million miles from the rest of the world. Fear and emotional exhaustion did that to you; pushed you out of the herd, isolated you.

'I thought he was going to die,' she said suddenly, voice husky.

Brodie turned and smiled at her. 'I know. But he's a fighter—he wants to live now, that's a big help. You have to be motivated; to have a reason to live, Donna. And your father's got one now.'

She wasn't really listening. She was noticing that he had had a quick shave while she was in the bathroom. His skin looked smooth and cool; sunlight showed her the graining of his pores, the angle of cheekbone and jaw. Her senses reacted so sharply that she suddenly got angry.

'What are you talking about?' she demanded, scowling at him.

'He wants to be here to see his first grandson,' Brodie told her with teasing amusement.

'What?' She felt herself flushing. She had forgotten all about what had happened just before her father collapsed. Fear had wiped her memory clean. Now it came flooding back and her hands clenched at her sides.

'Where did he get that crazy idea? Did you tell him you were bringing me home? That we were going to get married after all?'

'I haven't been in touch since I left to catch up with Gavin! It was just wishful thinking on your father's part.' He still looked amused, though, and Donna resented that.

'Why didn't you tell him it wasn't true?'

'Why didn't you?' he countered drily.

'I was speechless!'

'So was I,' he said with a blandly grave expression, and her head almost exploded with fury.

'You liar! You thought it was a big joke, I can't think why!'

'If you'd seen your face you'd know why,' Brodie assured her.

She looked at him with intense dislike and said through her teeth, 'Well, because of your stupid sense of humour my father's got the wrong impression and how on earth are we going to tell him it isn't true?'

'We aren't,' he said coolly.

Mrs Eyre came into the room while Donna was digesting that remark. She deftly laid the table, apparently oblivious of the fact that they were staring at each other in a blank silence.

'Your eggs will be another two minutes,' she said, going out.

'Thank you, Mrs Eyre,' said Brodie.

The door shut behind her. Donna said in a hoarse voice, 'What do you mean, we aren't? Of course we must! Sooner or later he's got to realise it isn't true.'

'Not while he's in danger of having another heart attack,' said Brodie, sitting down at the table as casually as though they were merely discussing the weather. He poured himself some orange juice from the iced jug, then filled her glass, ice clinking as he poured.

'We've got to tell him,' whispered Donna, appalled.

'Do you want to run the risk of causing a relapse?' Brodie buttered a slice of toast, took a sip of juice.

She must have been slow-witted after all the worry of the last twenty-four hours, because it was only beginning to dawn on her now that she was caught in a trap.

She leaned on the back of her chair, biting her lip. 'But sooner or later he's got to know . . .'

'It will have to be later.' He began to eat his toast as though that disposed of the subject, and Donna stared at him, maddened by his air of cool assurance, by the blithe disregard of how she felt. Mounting anger seemed to press against the top of her skull; she saw him through a red mist of pure temper.

'If you think for one minute that I'm going to pretend I even like you, you're crazy!' she seethed, turning to leave the room.

Mrs Eyre reappeared with a tray and looked at Donna in surprise. 'Your eggs,' she said with a faintly pitying kindness, as if Donna was out of her mind but it was only to be expected under such strain.

Donna sulkily sat down, managing to mutter, 'Thank you,' as the housekeeper placed her eggs in front of her.

There was a barbed silence until Mrs Eyre had left the room. Donna didn't look up; she cut off the top of her egg and ate without really tasting a spoonful.

Only when she had finished the first egg did she ask, 'What are you going to do about the money Gavin took? You said it had to be back in the account before the auditors started work.'

'It is back.'

'How? When.' She stared at him incredulously.

Brodie poured himself some more coffee and refilled her cup. 'I put it back before I took off for Paris,' he answered as calmly as if he were giving her the latest weather forecast.

She made a strangled noise, her eyes enormous and her face dark red with fury.

'Something go down the wrong way?' he enquired in concern.

'You put it back *before* you came to Paris?'

'Eat your egg before it gets cold.'

'You lied to us!'

'Mrs Eyre won't be very happy if you don't.'

'Why didn't you tell Gavin? Why did you pretend you hadn't put it back?'

'This toast is cold,' he murmured, buttering another slice.

Donna slammed her chair back and got up. 'Will you answer me? Stop playing games!'

Brodie put down his toast and wiped his fingers on his napkin. 'You'd better go to bed and get some sleep. You're worn out.'

Her voice had a raw quality by then. 'Answer me!'

He leaned back in his chair, considering her with wry eyes. 'I replaced the money from my own account as soon as I realised Gavin had bolted. If I'd told him do you really think he would have learnt anything? I wanted to scare him into starting to think. Gavin has to learn to face up to himself, to the consequences of what he does. Why should he just lift sixteen thousand pounds and get away scot free?'

'Then why did you put it back?' she asked.

'Because I didn't want your father embarrassed by a public scandal.'

'You have no right to take over our lives like this!' she said hoarsely. 'Fixing this, fixing that, giving Gavin orders—pushing me around. Who the hell do you think you are?'

'You're tired, go to bed.' Brodie got up; a tall, lean man with a coolly impervious face set in lines of authority.

She resented him visibly, her eyes flashing with temper. 'Stop telling me what to do!'

'Don't be obstinate, Donna.'

'I'll be what I like, do what I like,' she muttered in confused irritation. 'I won't dance to your tune.'

'Won't you?' He was coming towards her and she found that far too disturbing. Sometimes Brodie reminded her so much of her father; that cool insistence on his own way, that ruthless self-assertion. She looked at him with hectic eyes.

'I want to have this out now. You're not manoeuvring me into pretending we're back together again!'

'What do you suggest we do? Walk into your father's room at the hospital and tell him he made a mistake, we aren't reconciled?' The dry voice made her nerve ends flicker with angry fire, but what he said had the deadly ring of fact. She couldn't do it, of course. She couldn't risk upsetting her father. She looked at him with homicidal yearning.

'I'd like to kill you!'

Brodie's eyes flashed; dark, burning blue, infinitely alarming. He took hold of her waist with one arm and lifted her bodily as if she were a featherweight, an arm under her back.

'Put me down!' she gasped, taken aback.

He took no notice, carrying her out of the room too fast for her to have time to grab anything to hit him with.

Mrs Eyre was coming across the hall. She stared in amazed consternation at Donna's wriggling, kicking body.

'I'm carrying her up to bed, she's feeling rather faint,' Brodie explained smoothly, smiling.

Donna made a noise like a kettle coming to the boil, but went limp and stopped struggling, under the housekeeper's curious gaze.

'Would she like a hot-water bottle? Some warm milk? If there's anything I can do . . .'

'Thank you, Mrs Eyre,' said Brodie, going up the stairs, one eye on Donna's brooding, ominous expression.

When they were out of earshot of the housekeeper she said tersely, 'One day . . .'

His mouth twisted. 'Yes, one day,' he murmured, and she had a sudden stab of apprehension as she heard the way he said that. What did he mean? Not what she had meant, she was sure of that.

He carried her into her own room and put her down on the bed, but he didn't move away, he knelt above her, holding her shoulders down on the pillows, his face inches from her own.

'Get out of my room,' muttered Donna avoiding his gaze. Her throat beat with a frantic pulse; she hoped he couldn't see it.

'Don't you want me to help you get undressed?' he taunted.

'Lay one finger on me and . . .' Her ragged voice died away in sheer confusion under his curling smile. He thought he was so funny!

'What's the matter, Donna? Why are you so worried about having me in your bedroom?' His eyes were fixed on her neck; she tried desperately to still the rapid beating of that telltale pulse. Her helpless reaction to him wouldn't matter so much if it weren't visible, but her body betrayed her all the time.

'Mrs Eyre will be shocked,' she muttered.

'I doubt it. We're both adults, and she thinks the same as your father, remember.'

'I'll tell her the truth!'

'Not until we've told your father,' he contradicted flatly. 'She might say the wrong thing to him, even if we warned her that it was all a mistake. We'll explain to her once your father knows, but not before.'

'No, that's going too far,' she said furiously, trying to sit up, but he held her down on the bed by the weight of that powerful body. 'Let go of me, will you? I won't be manhandled by you!'

He was too close; she didn't want to see his hard-boned face inches away from her. She didn't want to be forced to notice the pared strength of cheekbone and jaw, the sensual potential of that firm, male mouth. One brief glance was enough to send her stupid pulses wild again.

'She may talk about it, tell people—the next thing I know, I'll be reading the announcement in *The Times*.'

'You're overreacting,' Brodie assured her, but there was a glint in his eye that made her very nervous.

'Will you let go of me?' she mumbled, trying to unlock the grip of those strong hands. 'You're going to leave bruises on my shoulders.'

'Where? Let me see,' he said, his hands moving down to unbutton her shirt, putting on a contrite expression.

Donna knocked them away, seething. 'Get out of here!'

He sat up, one hand raking back his ruffled black hair. 'I'll tell Mrs Eyre to let you sleep, not to wake you. Don't worry about your father. I'll keep in touch with the hospital, and if there's any news I'll wake you up to hear it.'

'Aren't you going to sleep?' He had been awake all night too. He showed far less sign of that than she felt.

'I may catch an hour or two, but I have to go to the office. Today is the start of the annual audit.'

Her face lost colour. 'Oh, yes, I'd forgotten. You're sure the books are okay now?'

'Quite sure. They won't query the movement of a large sum in and out of the account—that's what the private account is for: a temporary transfer of funds without needing to go through the long rigmarole of using the company accounts. As long as the books balance and the money is accounted for, there will be no problem.'

'You might have told me that in Paris, instead of letting me worry myself sick about Gavin!' she snapped crossly.

'Would you have come back if I had?'

Donna lay there, her fair hair tumbled across the pillows, looking at him angrily.

'No!'

He shrugged. 'That's what I thought.'

'You're despicable,' she told him in a low, shaky voice.

'I had good reasons for wanting you to come back.' He unknotted his tie and Donna stiffened, watching him warily.

'So that I could persuade my father to make Gavin see a psychiatrist, you said—what was the real reason?'

And why was he undoing his shirt collar? she wondered, but didn't ask because if he laid one finger on her again she'd scream until not merely Mrs Eyre but the whole village came running to find out what was going on.

'That was one very good reason,' he said casually, unbuttoning the rest of his shirt.

'What do you think you're doing?' she burst out, ready to jump off the bed if he came any closer.

'I'm just going to have a bath,' he said, getting up. He paused, eyeing her taken-aback expression. 'What did you think I was going to do?'

'Oh, get out!' yelled Donna, throwing a pillow at him. Brodie went, grinning, and it didn't make her feel any happier to follow him to the door and bolt it once he was outside.

She slid out of her clothes, tense with rage. She might have known that Brodie was up to something. He had been lying to her and Gavin—playing some complex game of his own and using Gavin's folly to trap them both. She had been a fool to take his bait and let him lure her back here. She had been on her guard from the minute she set eyes on him, but it hadn't done her much good. She had still fallen for his plausible lies, exactly as she had before.

But what was behind it this time? Naked, she paused, her face stiffening, 'Oh, no,' she whispered. 'He couldn't . . .'

He couldn't still hope to talk her into marrying him? Could he?

Hadn't she made her views on him very clear two years ago? He must have armour-plating to be able to forget what she had said to him, the insults she had hurled at him. How could he think he would ever get her to marry him, after that?

She went over to find a nightdress in the tall Georgian chest of drawers. Mrs Eyre had unpacked her clothes and put them neatly away. She pulled a short white cotton nightshirt out and was about to drop it over her head when she caught sight of her reflection in the long mirror in the corner of the room.

That was when she saw that her breasts had hardened; the nipples darkly pigmented against the pale gold of her flesh. She closed her eyes angrily, bitter stabs of desire penetrating her. Brodie wasn't stupid. He must have known what was happening to her while he held her down on the bed, watching her with those hooded blue eyes. She hated and despised him, but he was in her bloodstream. She had told herself for two years that she was free of the disease; cured for ever. She had lied, deceived herself. At the first opportunity it got the addiction had resurfaced; the yearning had begun again. From the minute she saw him in her apartment in Paris, she had been torn apart by the old craving. A few minutes ago she had felt it so painfully that she had had a hard job of hiding it, but Brodie was far too clever not to have picked up her hidden feelings.

If he did realise that in spite of her anger and her open dislike, she still felt a deep attraction towards him, it would explain why he hadn't given up on the idea of marrying her. He had made it clear that Gavin was never going to run the firm, but Gavin and herself would inherit the family shares, controlling the company. Brodie would want those shares badly. Without them his hold on control was weak. Once their father was out of the way they could always get rid of Brodie.

She pulled the nightshirt over her head and ran both hands over her weary, disturbed face. She felt almost as distraught as she had two years ago, when she first found out the sort of man Brodie Fox really was. She had been on the point of getting engaged to him when she met a girl as a party given by old friends of Brodie's. Donna had gone alone, but Brodie had promised to meet her there—he had been held up by a strike threat at one of the factories.

Brodie's friends were a married couple—Tom Reed, a wealthy stockbroker, and his wife Jinny. They lived in a spectacular house in Virginia Water and made a big fuss of Donna, insisting on showing her around, making sure that she had a glass of champagne and a plate of delicious hors d'oeuvres, introducing her to other guests. While she was circulating, chatting to people, she kept seeing another girl who didn't come over to her but who watched her oddly from a distance. What struck Donna was the other girl's beauty—it was the opposite of her own and far more obvious. Tall, sexily dressed in a scarlet silk dress, she had rich silky black hair and liquid black eyes—her figure was attracting quite a bit of attention, but she seemed indifferent to the men who kept trying to chat her up.

Donna perched on a window-seat when she was tired of wandering around the room and a moment later the other girl came over.

'You're Donna Cowley, aren't you?'

Donna gave her an uncertain smile. 'Yes, how did you know?'

'I've seen a picture of you. I'm Christabel Clair, by the way.'

Donna did a double-take, realising then why the other girl had been so familiar—Christabel Clair was a well-known photographic model.

'I should have recognised you,' she had said, offering her hand. 'I knew I'd seen that face somewhere. Where did you see a picture of me? I'm not famous.'

Christabel had hesitated before offering her own hand and her fingers had been icy cold.

'Brodie showed me a picture of you.' Something in the quiet bitterness of the voice made Donna freeze. As if she had a premonition she felt like getting down off the window-seat and running away, but she was too sensible to give in to such crazy impulses, so she went on smiling politely.

'Brodie? You're another friend of his?'

Christabel gave a hard laugh. 'A friend? No, I wouldn't call myself that, exactly.' She suddenly lifted her right hand and Donna stared blankly. Christabel

was wearing a ring on it; one big diamond surrounded
by a number of smaller ones. It glittered as she moved
her hand: cold, icy, beautiful.

'He gave me that.'

Donna's mouth had gone dry with fear. She had
looked from the ring to the girl's lovely face, and that
was when she saw the hostility behind Christabel's
tight smile.

'I thought of sending it back after he broke off our
engagement but I was too angry.'

Donna swallowed, shaken. 'You were engaged to
Brodie? When?'

Christabel kept her eyes on Donna's pale face; her
smile was acid now. 'For six months before he met
you—we were going to be married last week. I'd even
bought my wedding-dress. But then he was introduced
to you and decided I wasn't good enough for him.' She
snapped open the little silver evening-bag she was
carrying in one hand and produced a folded piece of
paper. 'He sent me that the day after he first met you.'

Donna hadn't wanted to take the paper, drawing
back from it, but Christabel had impatiently pushed it
into her hand. 'Read it! Go on, read it! You ought to
know what Brodie's really like. I've no doubt he's
fooled you the way he fooled me!'

Pale, her fingers trembling, Donna had unfolded the
creased piece of paper. It had been written on the firm's
stationery, and she recognised Brodie's handwriting.
There was no doubt about it, he had written it. It was a
brutally brief note. First a scrawled date—she hadn't
needed to check her diary to realise that Christabel had
spoken the truth; Brodie had written this the day after
he first met Donna. That had been a landmark in her

life, she couldn't have been mistaken about that date, the day she first met Brodie. Below the date a few callous words.

We won't be getting married, Christabel. It's over. I don't want to see you again, and don't make a fuss, it wouldn't do any good. I'm going to marry someone else.

She had stood there, staring at his name; hurried black scrawl right across the paper. Brodie.

Christabel had taken the note back abruptly, and Donna had looked up, blank-faced with shock.

'You had what I couldn't give him,' Christabel had said bitterly. 'Money, status, a future—I didn't have any of them. I hadn't made it in modelling then; I was just getting a few jobs. Brodie's ambitious, he couldn't wait to see how my career worked out. He's always been in a hurry to get to the top and you looked like an easier ladder, but if I'd been the one with money he'd have stayed with me, I'm certain of it. We were terrific in bed—it really worked with us. You'll never turn him on the way I did, for all your money.' She looked Donna up and down, her lips curling, 'I'm sorry for you, Miss Cowley. If you love him, you're going to have a tough life with him. I'd think again if I were you. You may buy Brodie, but you'll never own him.'

She had laughed, then turned on her heel and walked away, and Donna had sat there white-faced for a while until she felt able to walk away herself. She had somehow managed to smile politely at her hostess and explain that she had a headache and couldn't wait for Brodie any more. She was going home, Jinny had looked worried and asked if there was anything she could do—Donna had wondered if Jinny had noticed Christabel talking to her and been shaken. No doubt all his friends knew Brodie had been engaged before; no doubt they had all been whispering about it behind her back, wondering how long it would be before she found out.

She had forced a smile and said it had been a lovely party, she'd had a wonderful time, but she had to go now, her headache was so bad. Jinny had followed her to the front door, still concerned, and Donna had been deeply relieved to get away from her, from the bright lights and laughter, the music and cheerful voices. She had driven home and gone to bed, and next morning she had gone away for a couple of days to give herself time to think.

She knew she couldn't marry Brodie after discovering that he had so callously broken an engagement to another girl as soon as he had met someone richer. That wasn't what she had to decide.

The question was: *how* should she tell him she wouldn't marry him? She could simply tell him she knew about Christabel, had read that note, knew the whole story—but that would be so humiliating, it would tell him she was hurt and jealous and angry. It would make him think that all he had to do was soothe her down, reassure her, wind her round his little finger.

If she didn't tell him why she no longer wanted to marry him what *was* she to say? And how was she going to explain to her father that she wasn't going through with the marriage?

After two days of sleepless thinking and crying and coming up with no answer she had gone home and Brodie had been with her father.

Oddly, it had been very easy. Brodie had wanted to know where she had been—and with whom. He had been dark with rage.

Her father had been glowering at his side; in one of his more icily bullying moods.

Donna had refused to tell them where she had been or why or with whom; she had refused to tell them anything. Her father had stamped out, saying, 'You talk to her, Brodie. Get some sense out of her.'

Brodie had demanded an answer, but Donna had refused to give one. Instead she had taken off his ring and thrown it at him, then she had told him at length what she thought of him. She hadn't known that she could be so fluent. She hadn't realised until then the painful depth of her hurt and her anger.

Brodie had stiffened as he listened; first white, then an angry dark red, staring at her as if he couldn't believe his ears. She hadn't given him a chance to interrupt, to ask any questions, to protest. When she finally ran out of insults she turned on her heel and walked out, slamming the door behind her.

Of course, that hadn't been the end of it. Neither Brodie nor her father could believe she meant it. They saw her outburst as a fit of female rage. They tried to soothe her, to coax and wheedle her, to find out what had happened, why she had turned against Brodie so suddenly.

Donna had become silent; obstinate, dogged. She had made her arrangements without telling them what she meant to do and then one day left for Paris. Her French had always been good; she decided to become fluent and get a job in France, where she had always felt at home. She had known she couldn't stay in London, where she ran the risk of seeing Brodie all the time. She had to put space between them if she was to learn to forget him. Over the past two years she had been stupid enough to think she had managed it; that Brodie was just a dark shadow in her past, locked away and forgotten.

Now she knew how wrong she had been—Brodie wasn't locked away. He had sprung out, like a jack-in-the-box, and Donna wasn't safe any more. If Brodie had guessed that, she was in more danger than she had ever been before, because this time if he turned on the heat she might wake up to find herself married to a man she did not trust or like but who had a dangerous power over her senses.

CHAPTER FIVE

DONNA didn't wake up until the middle of the afternoon. After a cool shower she dressed in a pair of white cotton trousers and a blue tabard, put on some make-up and went downstairs. She found Gavin in the garden wandering around with his hands in his pockets and a worried look on his face.

'Oh, hi!' he said, turning to face her. 'Had a good sleep?'

'Yes—where did you get to this morning?'

He shrugged. 'Went for a walk. I needed to think, and I don't find that easy around Brodie Fox.'

'No,' she accepted, her mouth taut. 'I was worried about you.'

Gavin grimaced at her. 'Sorry, Sis.'

'Have you seen Brodie since you got back?'

He nodded. 'We had a talk.'

'Did he tell you about the money?'

'Yes. He says there's no need for Father to hear about it now, so long as I stay put and don't run off again.' Gavin stared at her, his eyes fixed and strained. 'I can't go back to that office, Donna, I couldn't bear it. What am I going to do?'

'Did you tell Brodie how you felt about the job?' She didn't need to see him shake his head; she had known Gavin wouldn't be able to talk to Brodie, any more than he could bring himself to talk frankly to their father.

'What's the point, anyway? I'm not trained for

anything else. I should have done what you did—got out and got myself some training.' Gavin put a casual arm around her, making a face. 'I respect you for that, you know, Donna. Leaving, taking time to study and then doing a difficult job—I admire you for it. I wish I'd had the guts to do it, but I've never been able to stand up to Father.'

'Father isn't here,' Donna pointed out.

Gavin looked sharply at her, puzzled. 'Well, I know, but he's going to be coming back home quite soon. I mean, it wasn't a serious attack, was it? Brodie said he'd be home within ten days or so, although he'd have to take it easy.'

'Ten days is a long time,' Donna pointed out. 'There's a lot you can do in ten days—you could start seeing a specialist who'd help you fight that addiction to gambling.' She felt Gavin stiffen, pull away. She wound her hand through his arm and held on to him, going on lightly, 'You could investigate glass-blowing, find out where you could get some training.'

He laughed impatiently. 'You're kidding—I'm too old to start an apprenticeship.'

'How do you know? Have you checked up on it? You could go to a technical college and train—aren't there colleges who take older students? Gavin, sitting around daydreaming won't get you anywhere. You've got to get out there, make your dream a reality. Okay, if you find it's too hard or you just can't bring yourself to make the effort, at least you'll know yourself a little better. But whatever you do, you must get help with the gambling. It will ruin your whole life if you don't. It's a sickness, like alcoholism—it isn't your fault you've got it, but it will be your fault if you don't do something to get help.'

His mouth was turned down at the edges in sullen resistance. 'What are you saying? That I'm crazy? I'm not crazy, I just like to get away from here, grab a little excitement.'

'You know it isn't just that.'

Her grave voice made him angry. 'Oh, why don't you mind your own business! You know nothing about it.'

He pulled free and walked back towards the house, his fair hair gilded by the late afternoon sunlight. It gave him a halo. Donna stared after him, sighing. She hadn't done that very well. It wasn't going to be easy to talk Gavin into having treatment, and she hadn't been as tactful as she should have been.

She began to follow him, but found herself suddenly facing Brodie. 'Mrs Eyre thought she'd seen you out here,' he said, standing between her and the garden door through which Gavin had just gone. 'I just came from the hospital—your father's condition is quite stable now. They're pleased with the progress he's making.'

'I know,' she said shortly. 'I rang the hospital as soon as I got up.'

He was wearing a pale grey suit with a formal grey and white striped city shirt and a stiff white collar. The clothes were as immaculate and as expensive as all his others, and again she wondered how he could afford to spend like that. She knew so little about him, she realised. What had he done before he joined their firm? She had a vague idea that he had worked for another similar firm in the north, but Brodie had never been very forthcoming. He didn't talk about himself or his past—with good reason, no doubt.

'They thought he shouldn't have visitors until

tomorrow,' said Brodie.

'I know, they told me.'

His eyes raked her cold face. 'What's wrong now?'

Her eyes rejected his curiosity. 'I don't have anything to say to you, that's all.' She moved to walk past and he side-stepped, blocking her way again.

'There's one thing you might tell me,' His voice was dry.

'What's that?'

'Why you changed your mind about me two years ago.' He sounded calm; his curiosity was purely academic. She hadn't hurt him, because he had never felt anything for her. Marrying her had been good business strategy; it had gone wrong, and Brodie would like to know why so that he wouldn't make the same mistake twice. He was a clever man; he learnt from his mistakes, unlike Gavin—and herself. They were both idiots, it seemed; they couldn't shed their follies so easily, or live the way their minds dictated. They were stupid enough to follow their hearts; that made you weak and vulnerable, especially to people like Brodie Fox.

'I realised what a mistake I was making,' Donna said curtly. 'I thought I'd made that clear at the time.' She didn't want to see too much of him while she was back here; she was afraid of what she might have betrayed in her room a few hours ago. Brodie didn't need to have a diagram drawn—she was afraid he might have picked up enough clues already.

'Oh, you were very clear,' said Brodie, his mouth tense.

She shrugged 'Well then!' She tried to walk past again, but he wasn't letting her get away that easily. He caught her arm between finger and thumb and she looked down at it distastefully as if it were an insect landing on her.

'Get that off!' She flicked her fingers at it, trying to look cool. She did not want him to pick up any more echoes of her emotional reactions to him. Her face must not give anything away. He had once acted well enough to convince her that he loved her; surely she could act an icy indifference to him?

'I was too numb to think straight at the time,' said Brodie, without releasing her. 'It was only later that it dawned on me that I didn't really know why you turned against me, what I'd done to make you look at me as if you hated me.'

'You were just yourself, I suppose,' Donna said with acid sweetness, baring her teeth at him. 'And I'd realised a little late what sort of man you really are.'

'No,' he said tersely, shaking his head. 'Something must have happened. Something triggered it. What?' His finger and thumb held her like pincers; she winced, pulling her arm away.

She was free now, but made the mistake of going in the wrong direction. Instead of making for the house she backed further into the garden and Brodie advanced, making her agitation deepen.

'I thought about it for weeks,' he said in that cool, deep voice. 'I went over everything that had happened before you told me it was off—looking for the significant break in the pattern. There's always one; a moment when something breaks and after that things are different, whether you're talking about a stock-market graph or a love affair. Everything was fine between us that spring, but then it dawned on me that

just before you went off on your own you went to a party
at Tom Reed's place.'

Donna stiffened, paling. She should have realised
that he would try to work it out; he was brilliant with
tiny detail. Her father had often said so, Brodie was a
man with a careful, complex mind. He hadn't just let it
go; he had worried at the problem. Had he come up
with the right solution?

'I never made it to the party, did I? I got called in to
settle a strike at one of the factories—I remembered
then that I'd rung you at Tom's and he said you'd just
left. He made a joke about it—said I'd lose you if I
didn't pay you more attention. He was kidding, but
when I thought back to that night, after you'd gone to
Paris, I wondered if he hadn't hit on the explanation.'

Her eyes flickered away to hide the relief in them.
Brodie hadn't found out that she had met Christabel
Clair that night, after all. Obviously Tom Reed hadn't
noticed them talking. Or had he deliberately left out
that telltale detail? Why had Christabel been at the
party, anyway? The Reeds must have known about her
engagement to Brodie. If they were friends of his, why
had they invited Christabel along when they knew that
Brodie and his new fiancée were going to be there too?

'Was that it, Donna?' asked Brodie, an odd
roughness in his voice. 'Didn't I take you seriously
enough? Did you think I cared more about the firm
than you?'

She took another step backwards, disturbed by the
note in his voice, as well as by her own thoughts. Had
the Reeds been involved in what happened that night?
Had they deliberately set up a meeting between herself
and Christabel? Why would they do that?

'I didn't think—I knew,' she said coldly. 'You wanted to marry me because it would make you father's son-in-law, but that wasn't why I walked out. I went for my own reasons—because I suddenly knew I couldn't bear being your wife.'

His eyes glittered in a taut, hard face. 'Just like that?'

'I'd thought I wouldn't mind marrying you to please my father,' she lied hurriedly, shaken by that expression, 'but I woke up and realised I didn't have to let him run my life for ever. I knew you just wanted to marry me for business reasons, you're ambitious and cold-blooded enough to go through with something like that—but I'm not, and once I'd realised what a crazy mistake it would be I knew I had to get out of it.'

He was breathing harshly, his brows black and drawn above those ominous eyes. 'Cold-blooded?' he repeated through his teeth. 'You think I'm cold-blooded, do you? Maybe it's time you discovered how wrong you are!' His hands shot out and grabbed her shoulders, pulling her toward him in spite of her struggle to get free.

'Don't,' she muttered hoarsely, terrified of what would happen if he kissed her. She would lose her head, he would know she had lied about how she felt. He must not kiss her. She kicked him and he gave a grunt of pain, his hold on her slackening enough to allow her to break away, and this time she remembered to run towards the house instead of away from it.

Brodie came after her, but as she shot through the French windows into the sitting-room she ran straight into Gavin, who looked at her in surprise.

'Where's the fire?'

A second later Brodie burst into the room, and Gavin

stared at him with hard eyes, comprehension coming into his face.

Brodie stood still, staring back at him. 'I want to talk to your sister alone, Gavin.'

'No way,' said Gavin with sudden angry malice. 'Leave her alone, she wants nothing to do with you. How many times do you have to be told? Do you want it in writing?'

Brodie's hard-boned face radiated pure rage. 'Don't take that tone with me, Gavin! This has nothing to do with you.'

'While I'm around, you won't push my sister into doing anything she doesn't want to do,' snapped Gavin, bristling at the dismissive contempt in Brodie's voice. 'You dont scare either of us. You may have a lot of pull with our father, but as far as we're concerned you can drop dead!'

Donna slid her hand into her brother's and Gavin held it tightly, looking at her sideways. 'Okay, kid, no panic. I'll deal with him.' There was complacency in his voice, he grinned at her, cocksure and pleased with himself for having defied Brodie. He had never dared to defy their father. She couldn't remember him tackling Brodie head on before, either. This must be a first for Gavin, and he was enjoying it.

Brodie watched them both, his mouth crooked. After a pause he walked past them out of the room, and Gavin swung her hand to and fro, laughing.

'Hey! He backed down. What do you know?'

'Thank you,' she said, smiling indulgently at him.

'If you have any more trouble from him, let me know,' Gavin boasted, squaring his narrow shoulders. There was a flush in his face; a flush of triumph. 'That will teach him to push women around—he'll have me to deal with in future if he tries again!'

'I'll keep out of his way,' she thought aloud.

Gavin sobered. 'That won't be easy. He's moved into the house while Father's in hospital.'

'What?' Her voice rose sharply and Gavin shrugged, looking at her helplessly.

'He did that last time Father had an attack—Brodie said it was so that he would be close to the hospital and able to get there fast if anything happened. It takes so long to drive from London.'

'Did he just move in without your permission?' asked Donna, frowning.

'Can you see him asking my permission for anything? No, he just moved in and I knew Father would approve, so there was no point in arguing. Anyway, Brodie often stays here at weekends. He and Father shut themselves in the study and talk business for hours. He uses this house like a second home.'

'Or a hotel,' Donna said tersely. The thought of having Brodie under the same roof made her blood run cold. 'What about the office? Will he be commuting from here every day?'

'Why would he tell me? Last time he didn't go into the office for a couple of days, until Father was out of danger, I remember. He was on the phone most of the time, doing business from here.'

'And Father just lets him do as he pleases,' she mused, frowning blackly.

'You know Brodie's the sort of son he really wanted,' Gavin muttered, and she looked at him with anxious compassion.

'He loves you, Gavin, I'm sure he does—in some

ways the two of you are very alike.'

Gavin laughed shortly. 'Are you being funny? I'm
nothing like Father.'

'You don't recognise it because you can't see
yourself, but you both have similar personalities, and
that may be why you don't hit it off some of the time.
Father resents the very qualities in you that he has
himself; that's why he keeps nagging at you to change.'

'You're crazy,' Gavin said, but he looked shaken.
Perhaps subconsciously he had always known that he
was rather like his father; he might not want to admit
it, but wouldn't he secretly be aware of it?

He gave her a quick, almost furtive look, smiling
shyly. 'I thought over what you said about finding out
about courses in glass-blowing. You may have something there. I might check it out.' His voice was casual,
throw-away, deliberately off-hand.

Donna didn't want to be too eager. She smiled back.
'Great!' Having put the idea into his head she would let
him work it out without further interference. What
Gavin really needed was to start running his own life
without dictation from their father or Brodie. It might
actually help him to realise that their father wasn't as
perfect as Gavin had always believed.

'But I'm not seeing any doctors,' Gavin said flatly.

She didn't argue. She had to feel her way towards
trying to persuade him into thinking about it. Gavin
had the obstinacy of the weak—she suddenly wondered
if he had the weakness of the strong, too. Was that why
he had always let their father order him around? Gavin
obviously wanted another sort of life than the one he
had always had. His admission that he had always had
a secret ambition to be a craftsman, blow glass of a very

different sort, showed that. Did he gamble to fill an
emptiness in his life? Their father had a drive towards
success which he had channelled into his business. If
Gavin had the same drive but was drawn to other fields
he must have been angry and frustrated ever since he
began to grow up, but however much he resented his
father's tyranny he hadn't actually walked out as she
had. He had stayed there, pleasing neither their father
nor himself. Why?

She looked at him thoughtfully. Could it be that
Gavin loved their father too much to break with him
openly as she had done?

'I'm hungry,' she said. 'Have you eaten? Did you
sleep, by the way?'

'For a couple of hours,' he admitted. 'I don't find it
easy to get to sleep in daylight. I had a sandwich and
some coffee when I got up, but I wouldn't say no to
another snack if you're having one.'

'Let's go into the kitchen and see what we can find,'
she said, 'Mrs Eyre won't mind if I borrow her domain
for a little while. She used to let me learn to cook with
her, do you remember?'

'I remember eating some rock-hard fairy cakes you
made,' Gavin teased.

'What a lie! They were delicious!'

Gavin laughed at her. 'Well, I survived the experiment, but to be on the safe side why don't we have
something simple, like beans on toast, today?'

The kitchen was empty. Donna hunted through the
rows of tins in the pantry until she found some baked
beans, then she handed the tin to Gavin to open while
she cut some bread and popped it into the toaster.
Gavin put the saucepan of beans on the hob and they

found themselves some plates and knives and forks. It was a long time since they had relaxed together like this. As children they had been very close. Growing up had meant growing away, too, keeping secrets from each other, no longer sharing everything.

They ate in the kitchen and had just finished their snack when Mrs Eyre came bustling into the kitchen with a basket of freshly picked soft fruit from the orchard at the bottom of the garden. She stopped in surprise, seeing them.

'We just had some beans on toast,' Donna told her, feeling she had to apologise for being in the housekeeper's kitchen.

'If I'd known you were hungry, I'd have got you something,' said Mrs Eyre. 'You only had to ask, I'd have been happy to do it.'

'It was fun doing it ourselves,' Gavin murmured, and the housekeeper softened, giving him a fond look. She had always had a weak spot for Gavin.

'Well, is there anything else I can get you?' She took their plates and put them in the sink. Donna and Gavin shook their heads, getting up, feeling they were being politely but firmly turned out of the room.

'I'm going to make a summer pudding for your dinner,' Mrs Eyre told her, seeing Donna glance at the basket of fruit.

'Would you like some help with preparing the currants?'

'No, thank you, Donna, I can manage. That's my job.' Mrs Eyre had never liked having her in the kitchen. Donna had got under her feet too much. Occasionally, Mrs Eyre would let her spend an hour there, learning to cook something, but more often she

would say she was too busy and push her out of the
room. Donna had had to learn all her housewifery when
she began living in an apartment in Paris. That was the
first time she had ever been given the chance to find out
what domestic skills she could acquire.

In the hall, Gavin looked at his watch. 'What time
does the library shut? I thought I might drive over there
and see if they have any books on glass-blowing.' He
was self-conscious, a little sheepish, his ears pink.

'What a good idea! You might try the bookshop if the
library haven't got any books. Oh, I just thought—why
don't you ask the library if they've got a list of the
classes the technical school are giving: I remember
when Mrs Eyre did pottery at evening class one year
she asked me to get her a leaflet from the library—they
usually have the syllabus handouts on the counter at
this time of year, because the classes start in the middle
of September.'

Gavin went off, nodding, and Donna heard his car
start up a few moments later. She wandered idly around
the house, looking at familiar objects with a strange
sense of *déjà vu*—nothing had been moved let alone
changed. While she was in Paris her father's life had
gone on just the same, although she wasn't there. The
thought made her sombre. Paris seemed so far away;
her two years there had flown. Yet she had come back
here to find exactly what she had left behind.

Mrs Eyre knocked on the sitting-room door a few
minutes later. 'I'm just going shopping, is there
anything I can get you?'

Donna shook her head, smiling politely. 'No,
thanks.'

'I'll only be half an hour or so,' Mrs Eyre told her. 'Mr

Brodie should be around, if you need him. I saw him going upstairs.'

She vanished before Donna had realised what she had said. Brodie was still here? She had thought he must have gone out. With a shock it dawned on her that they were alone in the house. She simply couldn't face him again—the last time had been traumatic enough. She tiptoed into the hall, listening intently for any sound. She would go down into the orchard where she would be safely out of view of the house and stay there until either Gavin or Mrs Eyre got back. Brodie was bound to assume that she had gone off with one of them.

As she was creeping across the hall the telephone began to shrill and she froze, mid-step, shooting an apprehensive glance towards the stairs. What if Brodie came down to answer that? As if in reply, he called from somewhere upstairs. 'Mrs Eyre! Answer that for me, would you? It's probably my call to the office—tell them I'll be down in two minutes, ask them to hang on until I get there. I'm just getting a file from my room.'

Donna bit her lip. If she didn't pick up the phone he would probably come down to find out why it was still ringing. She ran back across the hall to the nearest phone and lifted it.

'Can I speak to Mr Fox please?' a woman's voice said languorously.

Donna's brows lifted. Was that his secretary? She sounded more like a *femme fatale*. Perhaps a telephone manner which was seductive had been one of the qualities he had insisted on for his secretary? Perhaps it wasn't merely on the telephone that she had to be seductive, Donna thought viciously.

'He isn't here at the moment,' she said in a voice tipped with ice. 'Can you ring again later?'

There was a pause. 'Could you ask him to ring Christabel as soon as possible, please?'

Donna took a sharp breath, her body stiffening. 'Christabel?' she repeated huskily, as if not sure she'd heard correctly.

'Yes, he knows my number,' the purring voice said.

There was a click. She had hung up. Donna slowly replaced her own phone, staring down at it as if it were a snake. Brodie was seeing that woman again—which meant that the affair wasn't over after all. He had gone back to Christabel the minute Donna was out of the picture.

Her mind raced like an overheated engine; coming up with one conclusion after another. He had gone back to Christabel and she had been ready to forget and forgive, had she? No doubt she had been waiting with open arms, damn her. Was that what she had been banking on when she came up at that party? Had she been hoping that by dropping a little poison in Donna's ear, she would get Brodie back?

And it looked as if she had been right! Oh, she had been clever, Miss Christabel Clair! What woman could have listened to what she said without feeling the sting of jealousy?

Donna had never forgotten a syllable of that conversation at Tom Reed's party. The words had been burnt into her brain. She had woken up at night, long afterwards, remembering them, maddened by them.

'We were terrific in bed, it really worked for us. You'll never turn him on the way I did.'

Donna groaned, closing her eyes, her teeth grating.

She hadn't wanted to believe it, even in the first shock of hearing it—but Christabel's smile had carried such conviction. Her black eyes had glittered—she had eyes that knew everything, and a body that advertised her knowledge. A full, luscious red mouth; rich black curls; a body charged with sexuality—Donna had looked at her and felt positively naïve. Christabel's stare had dismissed her scornfully, given Donna back the reflection of herself that she had taken to Paris with her and brooded over jealously for months. Compared with Christabel she had felt small and pale and washed out; an insignificant little mouse.

A thud of feet on the stairs made her jerk back to the present. She began to hurry towards the kitchen, to escape, but Brodie appeared on the stairs and looked down at her.

'Did you answer the phone?'

She nodded, unable to say a word.

'Was it for me?'

Her lips parted and snapped off the one word. 'Yes.'

'Are they hanging on?' He glanced along the hall. 'No.'

'Who was it?' he asked, looking curiously at her, puzzled by her grim expression.

'Christabel,' she said, the name hurled at him. She saw him start, caught the flicker of alarm in his deceitful blue eyes. He pulled himself together quickly. Of course he would; he had had plenty of practice at lying. The more you did something, the better you got at it, and Brodie must be a past master at deceit by now.

'Did she say what she wanted?' he asked casually.

Donna held on to her self-control. She wasn't going to scream jealously at him; she had more self-respect.

She wouldn't laugh bitterly, either, much as she felt like it, or tell him scathingly that he knew damned well what Christabel wanted—and what he no doubt gave her in private from time to time when he wasn't too busy. How could Christabel accept her situation? If their engagement was on again, Brodie had managed to keep it very private, and he couldn't have married Christabel without it getting to James Cowley's ears. Their affair was hole-and-corner, furtive, hidden from all Brodie's friends.

If Donna hadn't disliked her so intensely, she might have felt sorry for the other girl, but she wasn't saintly enough for that.

'She wants you to ring her back,' she said icily. 'She said you knew her number.'

Brodie shrugged. 'I don't suppose it's urgent.' He came down the stairs, apparently unaware of the fact that she was looking at him with loathing. 'Where's Mrs Eyre?'

'Out.'

'And Gavin?'

It was only then that she caught the glimmer in his eyes, the watchful little smile that meant he knew Gavin had gone out. Had he seen him go in his car?

'He's out too,' she said defiantly. If he thought for one second that being alone in the house with her was going to give him a chance to get at her, he could think again! Five minutes ago she had been agitated and on edge at the prospect, but that had been before Christabel rang. Now, Donna would have no problem keeping him at bay if they were marooned on a desert island for weeks.

'So we're alone,' Brodie said softly, coming closer

and looking at her through his thick black lashes, a coaxing smile curving his mouth. She eyed him coldly. Did he really think she would fall for that obvious stuff?

'What am I supposed to do now? Swoon?' she asked sarcastically.

If she had hoped to surprise him or deflate him she was disappointed. Brodie merely laughed as if he thought she was playing hard to get, running so that he could follow.

'I promised to prove something to you, didn't I?' he murmured, close enough to touch her now and looking down at her, a mocking threat lurking in the depths of his eyes.

Donna didn't get the point at first; they were thinking at cross-purposes. She had Christabel on her mind. Brodie had something very different, as she realised too late.

'Prove . . . what?' she stammered, thinking for one stupid instant that he was about to tell her about Christabel, deny it all, give her some plausible explanation which, of course, she wouldn't believe, but which she half hoped he might make at least half convincing.

'That I'm not cold-blooded,' he whispered an inch from her mouth.

She saw too late where he had been leading and tried to get away, but his arms had gone round her waist and as she twisted in his grip his mouth burrowed into her throat, just below her ear, the brush of his lips warm and tormenting. Her whole body seemed to shiver; every cell melting, her pulses wild with fever and her breathing totally haywire.

'Let go,' she mumbled almost inaudibly as his kiss travelled upwards, searching for her mouth. She was terrified by the waves of excitement pounding through her. She didn't want to feel like this. Was she so weak-minded that she could just forget what sort of man he was the minute he took her in his arms?

Still holding her with one arm, Brodie took her chin in his other hand and firmly drew her head round. Donna's eyes opened, she hadn't known they were shut until then. She looked dazedly at him, saw his hard face poised above her for a second. Those narrowed eyes watching her seemed to read her emotions at a glance, then his mouth descended and she was lost.

She had almost forgotten the sensual power of his kiss; it was a revelation to her, behind her closed lids flashed a lightning which lit up her own feelings and Brodie's power over her. His mouth moved hotly, possessive and demanding, and Donna was helpless to halt her own hungry response to him. Her body swayed yieldingly, her arms going round his neck, and she kissed him back with a sensuality which matched his.

Brodie lifted his head a moment later and Donna heard the ragged drag of his breathing above the hoarseness of her own—they sounded like people saved from drowning, their bodies weakly leaning on each other.

Her eyes drowsily opened and saw dimly. Dusk had invaded the house; she stared up Brodie, still clinging to him, her mind completely off balance, as if she were waking from a dream.

His eyes smiled. 'Did I prove my point?'

She didn't know what he meant—everything that had happened before he kissed her seemed a million light-years back in the past.

'I'm not cold-blooded,' he reminded her huskily, and
bent his head to kiss her neck, a sharp desire in the way
his lips burnt on her skin. 'I want you, Donna,' he
muttered, his hands moving, touching her passionately.

She still had her eyes open and now her mind was
working, too. She remembered Christabel's phone call
with a stab of pain. How could she have been so weak-
willed, so stupid? She had been complacently telling
herself that she was armoured against him, he wouldn't
get to her again—but one kiss and he was under her
skin, back in her bloodstream. Hadn't he hurt her
enough two years ago? She must be a masochist to come
back for more, clinging to him like this, begging him to
hurt her again.

Cold-blooded? Wasn't he? How else did you describe
a man who kisses you like that when he's having an
affair with another woman?

'Well, I don't want you!' she spat out furiously,
pushing his head away and breaking free at the same
moment.

She caught Brodie off guard. He looked at her
blankly as if she'd slapped his face.

'I just wanted to see if I still fancied you, but I don't,'
she said with vicious iciness. 'I wouldn't touch you with
a bargepole. Stay away from me!' He had taken a step
back towards her, his jaw taut, the blue eyes flashing
rage. 'If you lay one finger on me again you'll have to
leave this house. I won't have you under the same roof
with me if I have to be on my guard all the time. You're
a guest here. This is my home. Just remember that.'

He seemed speechless, which satisfied her. She
turned on her heel and ran up the stairs. She should

have kept going, but her temper betrayed her. She looked back down at him, from the top step, her eyes molten with fury.

'Now you'd better ring your girl-friend before she gets impatient. You needn't keep her a secret any more—I'll make sure my father knows all about her!'

CHAPTER SIX

BRODIE'S face seemed to freeze; the cheekbones angular under the tanned skin, the mouth hard and straight, the blue eyes piercing as they stared up at her.

'What?' He dropped the word like ice into a glass, and Donna had a rush of fear to the head.

She turned and ran, knowing that he was coming after her, his long legs carrying him up the stairs faster than she was moving. She had a head-start, though; she got into her room and slammed the door and bolted it, leaning on it breathlessly, wishing to God she had held her tongue.

He crashed a hand against the panels and the door shook. 'Donna! Open this door!'

She backed, her eyes stretched wide until they hurt. She was furious with herself for having let him see that she knew all about his secret love affair. He might start thinking backwards, guessing too much about the past—she didn't want him to realise why she had broken with him and gone to France. Brodie was quite capable of using that information against her. Knowledge was power, hadn't someone said? It was far safer to keep him in the dark about her motives, then he coudn't think of ways of persuading her to change her mind.

'What did you mean by that? Open this door! You can't just chuck that sort of accusation at me and run away. Tell me what you meant. Donna, open this

door—I can't talk to you through it!' His voice was
hard and angry and she wasn't tempted to do as he
asked.

She sat down on the bed and stared around the room,
trying not to listen to him. Nothing here had been
changed, either—there were her books on the built-in
shelves in alcoves on either side of the bed; her
dressing-table still held bottles of perfume she had
never used, a set of silver brushes and combs which her
godmother had given her on her twenty-first birthday
but which she hadn't taken to Paris in case she lost
them; on the wall hung the same two pictures that had
always been there, prints of Pre-Raphaelite paintings,
one of girls with flushed, healthy faces lighting a
bonfire of autumn leaves and the other Millais' 'Blind
Girl' in a cornfield speckled with scarlet poppies.
Donna had gone to sleep and woken for twenty years
with those pictures above her head. When she was a
child they had been mysterious and intriguing; now
they held a poignant familiarity. Both of them had an
elegaic echo which haunted. Why had her father
chosen them?

'Donna, sooner or later you're going to have to tell
me,' Brodie threatened. 'If not now, next time you come
out of there. You don't really think I'll let it pass
without explanation?' His voice rose sharply. 'What
the hell did you mean?'

She turned her head suddenly, hearing the roar of an
engine on the drive. Gavin was home. The car braked,
the engine died, Gavin got out and slammed his car
door.

'Okay.' Brodie said curtly, 'I'll talk to you later. Don't
think I'll forget about it.'

She heard the thud of his feet on the stairs with deep relief, but it was only a respite she had gained—he meant what he said, he wouldn't forget or give up, not now that he had had a glimpse of what was going on inside her head. Why had she been so stupid? All this time she had held her tongue, not betraying what she knew, and then in an incautious moment of sheer rage she had given herself away.

She went to the window to get some air, but the evening was so warm. Laden with the fragrance of honeysuckle and rose, the air hardly moved. How many summer evenings had she lain in this room, breathing that heady sweetness, listening to the stillness of the night? Saffron Walden was out of sight across the green fields, but a few lights sprang up as she watched, in houses in the village down the road. She looked at her watch; it was still early and still light outside.

Was her father awake in his hospital bed? Was he frightened? She bit her lip—she had never got to know him very well, had she? She had resented his impatience with her brother. She always felt what Gavin felt; they were twins, after all, how could she help it? Their father hadn't been fair to Gavin; he had wanted him to be someone else, and that was never fair to a child. Gavin was himself; with all his faults he wasn't difficult to love—she had managed it easily enough. Why couldn't their father? If he had loved Gavin more end expected less of him, things would have been so different.

She heard the bang of the front door, and startled, she glanced down in time to see Brodie walking to his own car. He didn't look up at her window, so she could watch his tall, lean body without hiding what she felt.

He moved with power and grace, his body as streamlined as his car, as capable of speed and dynamism too. Her mouth went dry with desire and she was instantly furious with herself. When would she learn?

He got behind the wheel, the engine flared, the car shot away at a terrific speed, churning up gravel. Where was he going in such a hurry?

Donna's mouth twisted cynically. To see Christabel, of course—where else? To placate her, no doubt, tell her she needn't be jealous, Donna didn't mean a thing to him. Or perhaps Christabel didn't know she was back! Had Brodie been going to spend the weekend with her—and cancelled their plans to go to Paris? Was he hoping to keep Donna's return from Christabel as long as possible?

Donna knew the other girl was still one of the top models, her face appeared in women's magazines from time to time and Donna always flipped over the pages averting her eyes. She hadn't wanted any reminders of Christabel.

Her eyes watched his car disappear, then flicked over the beautifully kept gardens; the billiard-table smooth lawns, the cypresses on each side of the gate, the roses and the white marble fountain playing among the shrubs. All this was a symbol of her father's wealth and status—this was what Brodie wanted so much that he was ready to sacrifice his self-respect, even his deepest feelings, for it.

She didn't understand how he could want anything so worthless so much. There was more beauty in a violet growing in a hedge. There was more happiness in a tiny flat shared with someone you love, more pleasure in eating a hot-dog walking in the rain in a city street. A thousand things meant more to her than money or power. Why did Brodie want them so badly?

He must love Christabel, or he wouldn't have gone back to her. Donna hated admitting it, but it was dogged insistence on facing up to things as they really are that had sent her off to Paris two years ago. There was no point in living in a fool's paradise, and it was obvious that even though Brodie had sent Christabel that brutal note of dismissal he must be deeply involved with her or he would never have gone back to her.

Yet he wasn't prepared to marry Christabel, was he? They must have been together for some years now— how long had they known each other before he met Donna? Yet whatever his feelings, Brodie had pushed her aside with that callous shrug. What sort of love was it that could act like that?

And Christabel had to be crazy about him or she wouldn't have gone back when he snapped his fingers, knowing what she did about him. How could she do it?

She turned away from the window, her fingers curled inwards, her nails digging into her palms. She had no right to mock Christabel for being ready to forgive Brodie anything! Only a short time ago hadn't she herself been in his arms, kissing him back with hunger, clinging to him?

There was a tap on the door and she started. 'Donna?' Gavin's voice said uncertainly. 'Are you asleep?'

She ran her hands over her face to erase the emotions she had been feeling, and went over to open the door.

Gavin grinned excitedly at her, several books under his arm. 'I got three books—two from the library and

one from the bookshop in Saffron Walden. They're a
bit heavy going, but one of them has some useful
illustrations, and I did get a brochure from the
library—they had a pile on the counter, you were right.
The technical college opens again in early September,
but if I'm going to take a course I've got to enrol fast or
there may not be a place.'

She laughed at his breathless rush of words. 'Come
downstairs and we'll go through the syllabus while we
wait for dinner. Is Mrs Eyre back yet?'

'Yes, she's in the kitchen and there's a gorgeous smell
of steak and onions floating about.' Gavin gave her a
shy look. 'I called at the hospital. Father was asleep, but
they let me peep through the window in the door. He
looks better than I'd thought he would. They said we
could visit him tomorrow afternoon at three.'

Gavin had a very human need to love and be loved
which their father had never understood. Donna linked
her arm with her brother's and smiled affectionately at
him.

'Is he allowed to have flowers?' she asked.

'I think so. Should I have taken him some?' At once
Gavin looked guilty; he had failed in something again.

'Idiot—I meant we'll take him some tomorrow.'

He grinned. 'Oh, I get you. Right, we'll do that.
Come on, let's go through this brochure and find out if I
have to have any qualifications to take the course.'

'Are you going to discuss it with Brodie?' she asked
later as they were eating their dinner alone. Mrs Eyre
had come up with a delicious sirloin steak with black
peppercorns and fried onions followed by meltingly
light summer pudding which fell apart as you touched
it, spilling raspberries and redcurrants across the plate.

'He'd tell Father,' Gavin said sullenly. 'And they'd find a way of stopping me.'

'Let me talk to him,' said Donna, her eyes hard. It had just dawned on her that she had a weapon to use against Brodie—he wouldn't want James Cowley to know about his long affair with Christabel. If he wasn't afraid his boss would disapprove, surely he wouldn't have been so secretive about her for so long?

Gavin stared at her. 'What makes you think Brodie will listen to you?'

'Oh, I think he will,' she said with a cold smile. 'And anyway, he won't be sorry to see you out of his way, Gavin. If you take up a craft and stop bothering about the company that will be quite a relief for Brodie Fox.'

'That's true,' Gavin agreed, much struck by this thought. 'You're cleverer than me, Donna. I should have realised that a long time ago.'

'Everyone has a personal motive somewhere,' Donna said with a cynicism that made her brother frown.

'You've toughened up a lot since you went to Paris,' he said reproachfully.

'Grown up, maybe,' she shrugged, quickly smiling at him. 'Being away from home changes you. A little independence wouldn't do you any harm.'

'It hasn't been as easy for me to walk out on Father,' Gavin said, his face sober. 'I don't know why. I just couldn't do it. And now there's the sixteen thousand I owe Brodie—he put the money back himself, how on earth can I ever pay him back? I'll have to tell Father so that I can repay the money and, once Father knows, I'm back with my head in a noose, caught in the same old trap—not wanting to stay, not wanting to go. I've made a mess of my life, Donna.'

'For the moment, don't say a word to Father,' she said hurriedly, her eyes anxious. Gavin's confession could precipitate another heart attack.

'I'm not that much of a fool!' protested Gavin, offended. He yawned, looking at the clock. 'I'm going to bed now. It's been a hectic day and I haven't really slept properly for ages.'

Donna went to bed, too, but couldn't sleep. She lay awake listening for the sound of Brodie's car returning. He had been gone for hours now, she thought, sitting up to look angrily at the clock beside her bed. It was nearly one in the morning. Wasn't he coming back at all tonight?

Was he in bed with Christabel? The thought made her throw herself down again, on to her face, her hands screwed up into fists. She wouldn't be jealous, she scolded herself. Why should she lie here on edge with nerves when Brodie was with another woman, making love to her, perhaps talking about Donna, laughing behind her back?

She hated him, hated both of them, hated herself for going through this—next time she saw him things were going to be very different, from now on Brodie was dancing to her tune instead of the other way around.

If he wanted to keep his affair with Christabel from James Cowley, he was going to have to pay her price. Brodie knew that her father was old-fashioned—he might laugh at gossip about other men having affairs, but he would be furious if he found out that Brodie had pulled the wool over his eyes by having an affair while he was pretending to be in love with James Cowley's daughter. Her father would see that as a personal insult to himself.

Brodie would have to agree to help Gavin if he wanted her to hold her tongue about what she knew.

Donna must have drifted off to sleep shortly after that, because the next thing she knew was that she was opening her eyes to daylight and the smell of coffee right under her nose.

She blinked dreamily, then came awake with a rush as she realised it was Brodie holding the cup of coffee.

'What are you doing in my room? Get out before I scream the place down!' She sat up, clutching the sheet to her chin.

Brodie put the cup down on the bedside table and settled himself comfortably on the bed. 'Scream away. There's nobody in the house but us.' He linked his hands behind his head and surveyed her flushed face with quizzical enjoyment.

'Gavin!' she yelled. 'Gavin, come here!'

There was no answer. Brodie's smile mocked. 'He went for a drive ten minutes ago. Mrs Eyre's in the orchard picking gooseberries by the bucket to make into jam. You'd have to use a megaphone to get her to hear you.'

Donna held on to the sheet with fingers that trembled. 'Don't push your luck, Mr Fox!' she hissed. 'I'm getting very tired of your idea of a joke. Get out of my bedroom! If Mrs Eyre comes back and finds you in here she'll think . . .'

'Yes?' he asked softly when she paused in confusion, realising that it might be foolish to finish the sentence.

She felt her face stinging with hot colour and couldn't meet his eyes. The way Brodie was smiling didn't make her feel any less uneasy, either.

Donna pulled herself together with an effort. He thought he had her pinned in a corner, did he? Well, he was going to find out his mistake.

'I wanted to talk to you,' she began, and he unlinked his hands and leaned back on them, across her legs, tethering her to the bed.

'Good, I wanted to talk to you, too!' She didn't like the sound of that or the glint in his blue eyes. He had shaved recently; she looked angrily away from the smooth brown skin, the strong jaw and warm, masculine mouth. She didn't want any reminders of his sexual potency; she knew all about that. That was what got her into this tangle in the first place. From now on she wasn't going to let the sexual issue cloud her mind.

'About Gavin,' she said firmly. 'He wants to learn how to blow glass by hand, he doesn't want to work in the office any more, he isn't interested in industrial glass of the kind the company makes, but he is keen on learning the history of glass-making, the techniques of doing it today. My father isn't going to be too happy about it, but if you're on Gavin's side he may accept the plan, so I'll make a bargain with you . . .'

'Done,' he said quickly, too quickly. She stared at him in stupefaction.

'I hadn't finished,' she said warily—what did he think she had been about to propose? Had he realised that his affair with Christabel put him at risk with her father? Had he been about to suggest some sort of bargain about that?

'You don't need to—I like the idea. Believe me, Gavin's no addition to the work force—half the time he isn't there, and the other half he gets under people's feet and drives me scatty.'

Donna looked grimly at him. 'In other words, you're only too glad to get him out of your hair?'

He nodded. 'And when he's learnt all he can—or wants to—about glass, he could always come back as a consultant. I think it's an excellent idea, but of course I'll want something in exchange for my support. If I persuade your father to agree about this, I'll expect Gavin to see a psychiatrist. I still believe he needs straightening out, and I don't think he's going to stop gambling until he understands what makes him do it.'

She gave a little sigh. 'He may not agree to that.'

'Then you'll have to talk him into it. You have more influence with Gavin than anyone else does.' He glanced at the cup on her bedside table. 'Hadn't you better drink that before it gets cold?'

She picked up the cup with one hand, holding the sheet up with the other. Brodie observed her balancing act with dry interest.

'I saw Christabel last night,' he said conversationally.

The cup shook in her hand; a few drops of coffee splashed over the edge.

'Lucky that isn't hot any more,' Brodie remarked, his blue eyes ruthless as they watched her flushed face.

'I don't think my father would be too happy about your rather furtive private life,' Donna ground out between her teeth, glaring at him.

He sat up with a sudden movement that had violence in it, and she tensed, her eyes flickering. Brodie was alarming when he looked like that. Male rage was always unpredictable and hard to handle, especially when you were at such a disadvantage as to be half naked and in bed.

'All right!' he said tersely. 'What's this all about?'

'Ask your girl-friend!' she threw at him with bitterness.

His eyes were dangerously dark blue; the pupils dilated with fury. 'What do you know about Christabel and myself? Who told you?'

'She did.'

'Last night on the phone?' He looked baffled; furious but incredulous. 'Why on earth should she start talking about that on the phone? You've never met her, have you?' He must have caught something in the expression on her face, because he focused on her intently. '*Have* you?' he repeated, and she could see him thinking, the little wheels going round behind those blue eyes. Brodie was nothing if not clever, and she had given him a clue at last. 'You've met Christabel?' he thought aloud. 'Where? When?'

'Does that matter? I know what's been going on between you and I don't think my father would like it if I told him, do you?'

Brodie considered her, a harsh frown on his face. 'Are you trying to blackmail me, by any chance?' he asked slowly, as though the idea amazed him. No doubt it did. He was good at blackmailing people himself, but he didn't expect the tables to be turned, certainly not by her.

'You wouldn't like him to know the whole sordid story, would you?' Donna asked bitingly. 'His opinion of you wouldn't be so high after hearing that.'

'You don't think so?' he murmured, almost blankly, staring.

She laughed; the sound more rage than amusement. Did he still think he could talk her round?

'My God, you're cool, I'll say that for you,' she said

with contempt. 'In your place most men would be embarrassed, not to say ashamed—but you think on your feet, don't you? Well, if you're trying to work out how to wriggle out of this you can save yourself the trouble. You won't hoodwink me a second time!'

'When did I hoodwink you the first time?' he asked, and she saw that he was still trying to find out how much she knew and how she had heard about it.

'Never mind that,' she said impatiently, because the last thing she wanted was for him to realise why she had left him two years ago.

'I do mind it,' said Brodie with a snarl. 'I mind very much.' He leaned towards her and she shrank instinctively; the rake of his blue eyes made her skin grow cold. 'I want to know precisely what you think you're talking about and how you came to get this story.'

'Don't try to bully me! Unless you want me to go straight to my father with what I know!'

His smile held menace. 'You *are* blackmailing me . . .' He laughed shortly. 'I was beginning to get the distinct impression that you were.'

'I wouldn't call it blackmail!'

'No? Then what would you call it?'

'What do you call the way you got me to come back here from Paris?'

His mouth twisted. 'An appeal to family loyalty?'

Donna's smile was scathing. 'And what do you call the way you let my father believe we'd been reconciled?'

'Silent amusement,' he said blandly. 'I told you—I was afraid I'd laugh if I tried to explain he was wrong.'

She fizzed helplessly, longing to hit him. 'You expect

me to believe that? My father played right into your scheming hands—you're always looking for weapons to use against people. That's how you operate. Well, I've got a weapon to use against you now—and in future you'd better remember that!'

He shifted on the bed and she shrank against the bedhead, the sheet held higher. She felt very vulnerable in her flimsy nightie and the sheet was all the protection she had.

'You're scaring the hell out of me!' he mocked. She could see he didn't mean a word of it; his eyes held a secret enjoyment. 'But you still haven't told me what exactly you're blackmailing me with!'

'You know very well,' she said shortly. 'You and Christabel!'

He still gazed at her, his brows lifting in enquiry, and her temper flared again.

'I know you were engaged to her just before you met me!' she spat furiously. His face lost the smile and darkened.

'Who told you that? Christabel?'

'What difference does it make how I found out? You didn't tell me, did you? You never breathed a word about her, about having been engaged before.'

'It wasn't something I wanted to talk about,' he said curtly.

She laughed. 'I bet it wasn't!'

'Did she tell you why I broke off our engagement?' he asked harshly.

'Oh, yes, she told me that,' said Donna, swallowing on humiliation she didn't want him to see.

'Then you must see why I wouldn't want to discuss her when we first met—I was still too angry. I just wanted to forget her.'

Donna looked at him uncertainly; his tone wasn't quite what she had expected. He didn't seem to be on the defensive—on the contrary, he was looking angry.

Slowly she asked, 'What's your side of the story, then? I've only heard hers.' She didn't intend to believe everything Brodie said, but suddenly she wondered if there was an alternative explanation to the one Christabel had given her. Something didn't quite add up—Brodie's reactions to discovering that she knew about Christabel weren't what she had been expecting.

His mouth was hard, his eyes cold. 'I discovered she'd been away for the weekend with a married friend of mine. Is that what she told you?'

Donna's nerves jerked in surprise. She had been expecting some sort of plausible excuse, but somehow Brodie's words had a ring of truth—perhaps because she could hear the anger in them. Had Christabel been unfaithful to him, had he been jealous enough to decide to break with her and marry for ambition instead of love? She bit her lip, looking down.

'No, she didn't tell me that—but she did show me the note you sent her, and I did notice the date. You wrote that the day after we first met, didn't you? And you said you planned to marry someone else. Did you mean me? Did you decide to marry me there and then?'

There was a short silence. She looked through her lashes at his face; it was tense and angular.

'No,' he said flatly. 'The day we first met, Donna, I was too bloody angry to notice you much at all. I'd only just discovered what Christabel had been up to—it was the only thing on my mind. You hardly impinged at all.'

Hoarsely she whispered, 'But you decided to marry

me all the same because it would give you more power
with my father?' His words had stung, she felt her eyes
grow hot with unshed tears. How stupid to be hurt by
his admission—she had known for two years that he
had never loved her, why should she feel as if he had
slapped her round the face by telling her the truth?

'I didn't decide anything of the sort,' he said sharply.

'In your note to Christabel you said . . .'

'I was saving my face,' he snapped. 'How do you
think I felt? Finding out that she'd gone away with
someone else, that she was cheating on me with one of
my oldest friends, what do you think that did to me? I
felt a fool, to say the least. I wanted to hit back. I did
have a blazing row with the guy involved—we had a
fight and I lost my temper and broke his nose. He had
to go to hospital for a week, we narrowly escaped a
police enquiry. He lied, as much to save his own skin as
mine. His wife didn't know—still doesn't. I never told
her and I'm damn sure he didn't. But however furious I
was with Christabel I don't hit women, so I took out my
temper with a few terse words. I said I was marrying
someone else because I didn't want her to think she'd
broken my heart.'

'Had she?' Donna asked huskily, watching him
jealously. It was partly a rhetorical question—Christabel had obviously hurt him badly. Why, otherwise,
would he have beaten up his oldest friend? Who? she
thought suddenly. Who had Christabel gone away
with? But then no doubt the friendship had ended there
and then. Brodie wasn't likely to forgive the man
involved, so she had probably never met the man.

Brodie shrugged drily. 'I thought so for a few weeks,
but it was my pride that was wounded, not my heart.

Christabel's stunning—the most beautiful girl I've ever known, I think.'

Donna's lips tensed, her teeth gritted. She knew it was true; that didn't make it any easier to listen to.

'But she's like one of those tropical plants that have ravishing flowers; the first time you see them you're bowled over by them, but then you realise how gaudy and unreal they are, what shallow roots they have and how quickly they fade. There's a lot to be said for the English rose, its beauty lingers longer.' His blue eyes were on her face, caressingly moving from her eyes to her mouth in a leisurely scrutiny that made her flush. She pretended not to notice the insinuating compliment—he wasn't wheedling her into forgetting the obvious!

'But you went back to her after all that,' she said icily. 'And don't give me that innocent stare, as if you didn't know what I was talking about! She rang you last night and you rushed over to see her and stayed out half the night.'

'How do you know how long I stayed out?' he asked smoothly.

Donna's flushed face tightened. 'I do, that's all, and I'm not so naïve that I can't guess what the two of you were doing all that time! So don't give me any fairy story about having got over her, because it's obvious you're still just as involved.'

'Your imagination *has* been working overtime!' he drawled, moving even closer on the bed.

'And let go of that sheet!' Donna snarled. 'Get out of my bedroom before I hit you with something!'

'I'm shaking in my shoes!' murmured Brodie, laughing, and far from letting go of the sheet his hand slid down over her, moulding the sheet smoothly over her body, like a sculptor making a plaster cast with infinite care. The slow movement of that hand made her shudder with abrupt awareness, a pulse throbbing crazily in her neck.

'Stop that,' she muttered breathlessly.

Brodie watched the way the fine linen clung to her shoulders; her breasts, her waist, and her face burned at the way he watched.

'How long have you known about Christabel?' he asked in a soft voice, and Donna stiffened, but she didn't have to answer after all, because at that moment she heard Gavin running up the stairs. He must have come back without either of them hearing his car, which wasn't surprising considering their intense concentration on each other for the last half-hour.

Brodie turned his head, grimacing, and got up in a lazy movement.

He heard Donna's sigh of relief and looked wryly at her. 'Saved by the bell? Don't be too complacent. I'll talk to you later,' he promised, but at least he left the room a moment later, almost colliding with Gavin.

Her brother stood in the doorway, frowning, staring at her. 'What's been going on? Why was he in here?'

'We were talking about you,' Donna said evasively. 'He's going to help us persuade Father to let you take that course—but only if you agree to meet some tame psychiatrist of his.'

Gavin scowled. 'No way. I'm not going to any head-shrinker. There's nothing wrong with my mind.'

'Gambling's an addiction, Gavin,' she said gently. 'Like taking drugs or drinking too much. And it can be cured, but you need expert help.'

'I can stop whenever I like,' he said flatly.

'What harm would it do to see someone about it? It would be purely voluntary, you could stop going to see the doctor as soon as you liked, but if you agree to go at least once, Brodie will be on your side with Father.'

Gavin made an irritated face but shrugged after a minute. 'Oh, very well, but only once, mind. I'm not spending hours lying on a couch talking about my childhood or my dreams to some quack. If it means Brodie will talk Father into letting me leave the firm to start classes in glass-blowing I'll go through the motions anyway.'

Donna smiled at him, relaxing. It was some sort of progress.

CHAPTER SEVEN

JAMES COWLEY'S face seemed colourless against his pillows. His lips were sunken and pallid, his cheeks lined, his eyes half hidden under drooping lids. The Sister had already warned them that he was heavily sedated, they mustn't stay long or talk too much, but the weariness was still a shock to Donna.

She sat close to the bed and held her father's hand. 'Anything we can get you, Father?' she asked gently.

He whispered his reply, not moving. She got the impression he was afraid to move. 'No, thank you. I'm fine.'

Gavin stood behind her, looking miserable. He hated the atmosphere in the hospital and he was upset to see his father so ill.

'Brodie?' James Cowley asked with that care not to use up too much energy which betrayed his own fear.

'He's coming later.' They had been asked not to go in together. Two visitors were all he was allowed, Donna told him, smiling. 'Brodie is waiting outside. Gavin and I wanted to come in together.'

Her father's fingers pressed hers a little more tightly. 'You and Brodie—wonderful news. Always wanted it. Like a son to me.'

Donna managed a smile. 'I know.'

Gavin shifted resentfully, his eyes hurt. 'I'll let Brodie come in now,' he said.

His father looked up at him. 'Hardly seen you yet,' he said.

Gavin bent and kissed him awkwardly. 'You're looking great today, Father. Better than yesterday.'

James Cowley frowned. 'Did you come yesterday? I don't remember that.'

'You were asleep. I just had a peep at you.' Gavin sounded sheepish. Their father gave him a faint smile.

'Oh, I see. Thanks for coming, Gavin.' His eyes watched his son back out of the room; Donna heard his sigh.

Tentatively she said, 'You know, Gavin's studying the history of glass-making, Father? He's become really interested in it. I'd no idea how far back the process went. Gavin says Roman glass is a beautiful bluey colour, cloudy, because the process was so erratic. Too many imperfections, he says.'

James Cowley stared at her in surprise. 'He always did have a romantic streak; impractical, I'm afraid.' He sighed again.

Brodie joined them and she watched her father's eyes brighten a little. 'Good of you to come, Brodie. How's the order book?'

'No business,' Donna ordered flatly.

Her father frowned as petulantly as a sick child. 'I just want to know what . . .'

'No business,' Brodie agreed, smiling teasingly. 'You heard her. You don't want to get me in trouble with her, do you? She may not scare you, but she scares me!'

Donna bristled at the mockery but hid that from her father, who was chuckling delightedly.

'Start as you mean to go on, lad,' he said in his tired voice. 'Don't let a woman rule the roost.'

Donna pretended to laugh, but her hackles rose, especially when Brodie gave her another sidelong glance, his blue eyes gleaming with amusement, not at what her father had said, but at what he knew full well must be her reaction to it.

'Oh, I'll keep her under control,' said Brodie, winking.

This little masculine fun had one good effect—it put a trace of colour back into her father's face and he was really smiling now. Donna swallowed back the irritation she was tempted to express.

It wasn't until she and Brodie had left the room and began walking down the corridor that she turned on him, flushed and indignant.

'Don't do that again!' she snapped.

'What?' He opened blue eyes at her, innocent as a baby's.

'Don't give me that sweet stare—you know very well what I mean! All that stuff about keeping me in my place. I didn't say anything because I didn't want to upset my father and you knew I'd have to grin and bear it, that's why you did it.' She was angry enough to get confused, her words tripping over each other.

A student nurse came towards them, very young and pretty in her rustling uniform. She stared at Brodie, listening to them, as she passed, and he gave her a wink, as he had James Cowley.

'No need to get so grim about it. Your father thinks a woman's place is in the home. I was humouring him.'

'You don't think a woman's place is in the home?' she threw at him disbelievingly, suddenly realising that the nurse was listening and irritated about that too.

'Me? No, I think a woman's place is in a man's bed,'

said Brodie, grinning. The nurse gave a little giggle and pattered away.

'Typical!' muttered Donna, even more furious now. He was playing to the gallery again and she was sick of being his straight man. If he wanted someone to bounce jokes off he could find himself another victim.

They came out of the main doors and turned towards the hospital car park where Brodie had left his car. Gavin was sitting in it; he had fled the hospital ambience as soon as he left his father's room, obviously. He was sitting in the back of the car, his head back against the cushions, his eyes closed. Donna looked at him anxiously—had he been very hurt by his father's obvious preference for Brodie's company? Gavin opened his eyes and looked at her blankly.

'I think I'll go up to town and see a film tonight,' he said in a casual, offhand way. 'I feel like some bright lights.'

Donna got into the car, her face concerned. 'I'll come with you,' she offered.

'We'd better not both go in case there's an emergency call from the hospital,' said Gavin.

Brodie drove back to the house without commenting, but as he parked outside on the drive he looked over his shoulder at Gavin. 'Skip it for tonight, Gavin—go tomorrow. You're still tired and out of sorts. You'll feel better in the morning.'

That was a red rag to a bull. Gavin wasn't taking any advice from Brodie tonight.

'Damn you, mind your own business!' he snarled, and banged out of the car.

Donna hurriedly got out too, but he was already opening the door of his little sports car. By the time she could get over to him his engine was racing and he was moving away at a speed which made her jump out of his way with a startled cry.

'Oh, damn,' she muttered, on the point of tears, staring after him. Brodie loomed up beside her, frowning, and she looked at him angrily, her face pale and stiff.

'He's going to one of those clubs—he'll gamble again. Why didn't you try to stop him?'

'We'll try,' Brodie said in cool tones. 'Come on—run in and change into something pretty and we'll do a tour of his usual haunts. We'll find him at one of them, but they won't be open until around nine. Gavin will probably catch a film first, have a meal, then start gambling. We'll have plenty of time to get on his trail, so stop looking so desperate. It might not be a bad thing for you to see what exactly he's hooked on.'

She stared at him, biting her lip. 'How do you know where he may be?'

'I've had to pay some of his debts,' Brodie said drily, and she flinched. 'When Gavin doesn't pay they get in touch with his father—I take the calls and keep it from the old man's ears.'

'You knew he'd been gambling and you didn't put a stop to it?' she broke out, and Brodie gave her a long, hard stare.

'What do you suggest I should have done? Tied him up? Smacked him? Or told your father and got him to stop Gavin's money supply? I did what I could—I talked to Gavin, he promised he wouldn't do it again and for a while he'd keep his word, but sooner or later he'd break out again. The least pressure and he snaps. Do you think I don't know why he's gone off tonight?

Seeing his father upset him, didn't it? It's always the same trigger. You could almost say Gavin's allergic to his father. He loves him, but it's a destructive love. It's no good for Gavin, anyway.'

Donna listened soberly and had to admit that Brodie was shrewd in his assessment of her brother's problem. She nodded and said huskily, 'I'm sorry, I wasn't fair to you. I'd no right to say that. It isn't your fault, and I'm grateful for everything you've done for Gavin.'

She went into the house and upstairs to her bedroom to change into a dress more suitable for hitting the nightspots in London. She picked out an apricot satin, very low cut, leaving her shoulders bare and hiding very little of her breasts. The lustrous material gave a deep gold to her skin and heightened the colour of her blonde hair; she felt a little more cheerful when she saw herself in the mirror. Colour altered her mood; it always had. As a child she could remember sitting staring at a rainbow with rapt delight.

Her eyes were misty, faintly sad, even after she had smoothed a glittery green eyeshadow over her lids. She glossed her lips with a warm orangy pink, brushed blusher over her cheekbones—and tilted her head to consider the result. Well, she had given her face a little more colour, even if it was merely artificial. She looked as if she were going to a party now, but she found it hard to smile. She didn't want to go to London with Brodie, to scour the nightspots and gambling clubs for her brother. But even less did she want Gavin to stay out all night losing money he didn't have.

He was deeply in debt to Brodie already—how would he pay him back unless the money came from their father? Why did Brodie go to the trouble of paying

Gavin's gambling debts?

Anxiety and suspicion darkened her eyes, as she got up and walked to the bedroom door. What was Brodie up to? Where did he get all his money? That car of his, his expensive clothes, the sort of hotels and restaurants he frequented—all added up to money, and a great deal of it. Where did it come from? How could anyone afford to pay Gavin's debts to the tune of sixteen thousand and more when it was obvious that repayment might be a long time coming?

As she came to the head of the stairs she saw him waiting for her in the hall. There was only one lamp on; the dusk was still falling gently in the warm summer evening. By that soft light she saw Brodie look up at her, his black head gleaming, his eyes a vivid blue between their swept-back lashes. Her heart turned over and she could hardly breathe.

He had changed, too. He was wearing a black evening jacket now with a crisp white shirt and black tie. Formal clothes suited him; he looked even more striking in them. He came to the foot of the stairs, watching Donna walk down carefully, her long skirts lifted so that she shouldn't trip over them. She was intensely self-conscious under his gaze. She wished at times she really knew what he thought of her. Now and then she almost believed he did find her attractive—at others she suspected it was all pretence. His face was unreadable; set in that sculptured mask, the dark blue eyes fixed on her.

Nervously she stumbled into speech. 'We ought to tell Mrs Eyre we're going out before she starts cooking dinner.'

'I did. Told her to have an evening off for once.'

She gave him a sharp look. He gave orders here as if he were already master of the house!

Brodie caught the look; his smile wry. 'She saw me in my dinner jacket and obviously wondered what was going on—so I explained that I was taking you dancing.' His eyes mocked. 'She thought it was a very good idea, give us some time together. Mrs Eyre has a very romantic streak.'

Donna said crossly, 'You shouldn't let her get ideas like that! When she realises it was just an act, she's going to feel a fool—I know I would. I'll go and explain to her now.'

His hand looped round her arm, pulling her in the other direction, towards the front door. 'If we're to catch up with Gavin, we'd better get a move on.'

She let herself be led out to the car, but gave him an obstinate look. 'I'll tell her tomorrow, then.'

Brodie pushed her into the passenger seat of the car without comment and she settled down, arranging her full, shimmering skirts carefully. Satin creased too easily, that was the problem with it.

Brodie got behind the wheel and started the engine. 'Your dress is ravishing,' he said softly without looking at her. 'It reminds me of a peach, that colour—rich and luscious, and very tempting.'

She felt her face flow with colour. 'Thank you.'

He drove away, a smile curling his mouth, as though her reaction to the compliment amused him.

'Aren't you going to ask me what's so tempting?' he murmured.

Donna stared out of the window at the leafy hedgerows rushing past; pink campion and white rambling roses among the nettles and traveller's joy and the small pale stars of the nightshade.

He shot a quick look at her stubborn profile, then answered his own question. 'Most men will find the idea of peeling that dress off very tempting.'

She threw him a cold stare. 'Can we have some music? I don't feel like talking, especially if you're going to make remarks like that all the way to London.'

'Pick out a tape,' he shrugged. 'They're in the glove compartment.'

She flipped through the neat row of tapes she found and picked out some Gershwin piano music. Leaning back in her seat as the music began, she watched the sky turning a warm, purplish shade. Brodie drove in silence at great speed, his car moving smoothly along the motorway to London, eating the miles while Gershwin's melodies occupied the forefront of her mind. Under cover of that, she was able to worry about Gavin, about Brodie's taste for luxury and how he paid for it, about her father and the future for all of them. In Paris she had got away from this tangle; now she was caught up in it again, like a fly caught in a sticky web. With every day that passed she wondered how she was ever going to break free again.

When they reached London Brodie parked the car in the private car park of the first club they visited. They took the lift from the subterranean vault up to the top floor of the hotel that owned the club.

'Good evening, sir,' the manager greeted them, giving Brodie an assessing glance. 'A table? I'm not sure if we have one free—if you'd care to wait?'

Brodie took a step forward and glanced round the room; dimly lit and noisy with the clamour of a cabaret singer currently occupying the small stage. She wasn't beautiful, but she was throbbing with vitality and the audience obviously loved her, a ripple of applause and laughter kept breaking out. Donna was so busy staring at her that she didn't notice whatever Brodie said or did, but suddenly they were being shown to a table. How had he persuaded the manager to let them jump the queue? she wondered cynically. A discreet bribe? Probably.

Brodie ordered champagne and caviar casually, and Donna stared at him, all her suspicions surfacing again. How could he afford this? Did he come to places like this often?

'You don't really think we'll find Gavin here?' she said, and Brodie leaned over and said very softly in her ear, 'If you look in the corner you'll see some of his friends—the noisy crowd in evening dress, see them?'

Donna stared through the blue, smoky air. She didn't recognise the people at the table, but they were a type she identified easily enough. Two young men and a couple of girls; all very well dressed, flushed faces, a little drunk, rather silly, obviously wealthy.

'Gavin goes around with people like them?' Her mouth was stiff with distaste, as one of the men called a waiter over and ordered champagne in a cut-glass English accent that rang with arrogance.

'Lately he has, so I gather. They gamble, too—and make a nuisance of themselves in places like this. Having fun, they call it. Expensive fun for Gavin.' Brodie's mouth was hard with contempt.

'He'll never be able to pay you back unless he gets the money from my father,' Donna said suddenly. 'Can you afford to wait?'

He shrugged without answering, sipping his champagne.

She picked up her own glass and drank a little. 'I expect these people charge the earth for champagne and caviar,' she added pointedly. 'Does this go on the firm's expenses?'

'No, I wouldn't call you a legitimate business expense,' he said ironically, staring into her suspicious eyes. 'Now what's eating you? I know that look. What am I being accused of now?'

'I'm not accusing you of anything, I'm just curious— you seem to live very extravagantly. That car can't have been cheap and your clothes are very good. I suppose you feel you have to project a successful image, but it can't leave you much of your income at the end of a year.'

Brodie's mouth twisted. 'I see,' he said slowly. 'You wonder if I'm cooking the books? Embezzling your father's money, the way Gavin did?'

'I didn't say that!'

'The implication was obvious enough.' His face hardened.

'I merely wondered . . .'

'The answer is no, Donna,' he said curtly, his brows drawn above his fixed blue eyes. The frown made her nervous. She shouldn't have said anything—the only evidence she had was guesswork based on her own observation of the way he lived. There might be a simple explanation—perhaps he had money of his own? He had never told her much about his background. He was oddly secretive about the past, about his family, his earlier life. She hadn't noticed that until she met Christabel at that party and realised how little she really knew about Brodie. Until then she had been too wildly in love to think of anything but him—where he came from, what he was, didn't seem to matter.

'Do your family have money?' she asked, her eyes lowered and her face flushed.

'Have some caviar,' he invited coolly, pushing the silver dish towards her.

She wasn't hungry, but she took a spoon of the black pearls, a slice of lemon and a little chopped boiled egg. The toast was wrapped in a damask napkin and still warm.

If he thought she was going to stop questioning him, he was wrong, though. 'Are your parents alive?' she asked him, pushing the dish back to him. The salty taste of the caviar was perfect with the wine.

He helped himself, his eyes on her. 'No. Both dead.'

'Oh. I'm sorry. When?' She softened, her eyes sympathetic as she watched his face.

'I never knew them.'

Her head came up and her eyes widened. 'I didn't realise . . . you mean they died when you were very young?'

'Yes.' The admission was terse, the face rigid. Brodie didn't like talking about this and he changed the subject firmly. 'If Gavin doesn't show up here within half an hour we'll go on to the Rambouillet—he gambles there more regularly than anywhere else.'

She nodded, aware that he was putting up a no entry sign. Looking back, she realised how often he had done that in the past. Whenever she did come close to asking him questions about himself Brodie managed to steer her away from the subject.

This time though she wasn't going to let him shut her

up. 'How old were you when your parents died?' she insisted.

She saw the reluctance in his face—why was he so unwilling to talk about himself? What was he hiding?

'I was just a baby,' he said shortly, refilling her glass. 'More caviar?'

'No, thank you.' She absorbed what he had told her, feeling very shaken. What would such a childhood do to someone? Her own early years had been happy until her mother's death and the sudden icing up of her father's feelings towards his children. Looking back, she realised how much those first years had meant to her later—creating a golden image to which she looked back nostalgically whenever she was unhappy. Her early childhood had been radiant; the sun had always seemed to be shining. Perhaps it did for everyone when they were very young. But what had it been like for Brodie?

'Who did you live with, then?' she asked hesitantly. Had he been brought up in an orphanage?

'An uncle. My father's brother.'

'Did you like him?'

Brodie gave her a barbed smile. 'Not much, no. He didn't like me much, either. We existed in the same house and tolerated each other.'

Donna bit her inner lip, eyeing him uneasily. 'Was he married?'

'No. I suppose you could call him a convinced misogynist. There were no women in his house at all. Not that he liked anyone much—he was a surly, bad-tempered man, full of grievances, and very suspicious. I didn't have to put up with him once I was old enough to go away to school. As soon as I was eight, he packed me off to boarding-school and forgot all about me.'

'It must have been very lonely,' she said. 'Did you like school?'

'It was Okay. At least I had friends and wasn't always on my own.'

'Is your uncle . . .'

'He died when I was fifteen,' he interrupted, looking at his watch. 'We might as well move on now—if Gavin was going to come he'd be here by now.'

He turned and signalled to the waiter just as the cabaret began again with a pop group playing vibrant, noisy music of their own. Donna watched Brodie settle the bill and got up from her chair.

As they made their way out a new party arrived in the foyer next to the lifts. Their table wouldn't be empty long, Donna thought drily. The place was packed—she couldn't imagine why, because the champagne had been faintly flat and the music far too loud. Even the caviar seemed tired, but then some people liked this sort of place. It wasn't her own taste. Was it Brodie's?

It wasn't until she and Brodie were at the entrance that she realised that one of the group just arriving was Christabel Clair.

Donna felt her body stiffen in shock, her face tightened and the smile she hurriedly put on seemed totally phoney, but she wasn't going to let her real feelings show in front of either Christabel or Brodie.

A second after she had noticed Christabel, the other woman saw Brodie. Donna bitterly watched the glance they exchanged; even if she hadn't known about their private relationship she would have guessed there was something between them if she had seen that look. They hadn't been expecting to see each other. Their faces were unguarded for a second; Christabel flushed, Brodie became tense.

Christabel pulled herself together quickly. She was a wonderful actress, Donna had to give her that. She smiled radiantly and held out her hands. 'Brodie! Lovely to see you. It must be ages since last time.'

Brodie almost didn't take her hands, Donna noticed. Christabel leaned forward and kissed his cheek, or rather, brushed her cheek against his, making a kissing sound. Brodie's face was grim.

'Darling, don't you look gorgeous? Having a night out?' It was only then that Christabel looked from him to the girl with him and her eyes widened, startled, before they hardened and glittered like jet.

'Good heavens—it's Donna Cowley, isn't it?'

'Hallo,' said Donna with ice in her voice.

The other people with Christabel were a few feet behind her, watching smilingly. She saw a man nodding to Brodie and Brodie said something coolly polite in reply.

There were diamonds in Christabel's ears. She tossed her head back stagily and the jewels flashed; her laughter was just as unreal.

'I thought you lived abroad these days.'

'I do.' Donna couldn't bring herself to pretend like her; her hatred was too intense. Brodie had to be passionately in love with Christabel or he would never have forgiven her for being unfaithful to him, he wouldn't be seeing her again. Christabel had just said lightly that it was ages since she had seen him—yet Donna knew they had been together for hours last night. She knew Christabel was a fluent liar, but it still shocked her to hear such a smooth lie coming out of that beautiful, selfish, greedy mouth.

'I'm thinking of going abroad myself,' Christabel said, her eyes flickering to Brodie's stern profile and away again. 'I fancy the States, New York. That's where the action is, isn't it?' She laughed over her shoulder at one of the men in her party and he smiled back eagerly. Donna saw the surreptitious glance Christabel gave to Brodie as she turned back. She might be pretending to talk to Donna, but what she was saying was really for Brodie's ears. Was she threatening to leave him if he didn't marry her? wondered Donna bitterly. How would he react to that?

'Are you still modelling' asked Donna. 'It's a very short career at the top, isn't it?' The malice in her own voice made her feel ashamed as she felt Brodie give her a sideways look.

Christabel showed her teeth in a dazzling, hostile smile. 'Darling, modelling's only a stepping-stone to better things.'

Like sleeping with rich men? Donna thought viciously, her face flushed. She wanted to slap Christabel across her lovely, assured face, but she hung on to her self-control.

Christabel looked her up and down dismissively. 'What a colourful dress! Terribly sweet, isn't it, Brodie darling?'

Donna's teeth met. Her lustrous apricot satin seemed as gaudy as a marigold next to the sophisticated black silk which clung lovingly to every curve of Christabel's sexy body. Donna knew enough about style to guess the name of the designer; that dress had cost the earth. It was intended less to clothe a woman than to emphasise her sex appeal, and on Christabel it certainly did that.

Brodie put a hand under Donna's elbow, moving closer. 'We must rush, I'm afraid. Nice to see you.' He didn't look at Christabel, though, he smiled politely at the people behind her, her friends, who had been curious and silent throughout the little interlude. Did *they* guess at the secret relationship?

Angrily flushed, Donna let herself be steered past into the waiting lift. She felt that Christabel had won that round. She should never have let herself challenge the other woman; losing your temper was always a mistake with people like that.

The doors shut; they sank downwards smoothly, silently. Donna stared at nothing, her mind in turmoil. What had been going on between Brodie and Christabel back there? Was their affair really over this time? Or had they been playing some complicated poker game behind their smiles, a mixture of bluff and threat? Who had been the winner?

As the lift stopped and the doors slid back Brodie asked her, 'What are you brooding over?'

'I'm not brooding,' she denied with vehemence, walking out into the darkened, empty car park.

'No?' He sounded unconvinced, quizzical. She ignored that and walked towards his car, her footsteps echoing in the concrete vault above and from the solid concrete walls. Brodie kept pace without hurrying. She saw their black shadows leaping up the dimly lit walls in a strange, manic dance.

'Why did she lie about having seen you lately?' she broke out suddenly. 'It was such a silly, pointless lie!'

'Ah,' he said with mockery in his tone, 'it's Christabel you aren't brooding over—I suspected it might be.'

'What was all that about, anyway? Have you quarrelled again?' She tried not to sound hopeful. What did she care? Let him have an affair with anyone he liked. It didn't matter to her. She despised him.

He unlocked his car and held the door open for her without answering her questions, but as he drove up out into the lamplit street he murmured, 'It's too complicated to explain tonight—first we have to find Gavin.'

Donna gave a rough sigh. 'If he came to London.'

'I have a hunch we'll find him at the Rambouillet.'

'If we don't?' Her voice shook a little.

'Then we'll scour London until we do find him.' Brodie sounded so confident and calm. She resented it, for some reason.

'We should have followed him when he first drove away!' she said angrily. 'Your car is faster than his—you could have hung on his tail until he stopped.'

'Or crashed,' Brodie said coolly.

She looked at him, startled. He turned his dark head and his eyes smouldered between their jet lashes.

'Hadn't that occurred to you? If I *had* driven after him, what do you think he would have done? Put his foot down and driven like a madman and heaven help anyone who got in his way. Gavin can be a little crazy once he gets into the sort of mood he was in tonight. I wonder how well you know your brother.'

He parked again a few doors down from the St James's Club to which they had headed. 'Why don't you wait in the car while I take a look to see if he's there?'

'I'd rather come with you,' she said belligerently. 'I doubt if Gavin would leave if you asked him, but he might for me.'

'He will if I ask, too,' said Brodie with a menace that made her stiffen. 'Stay in the car, Donna. It would be wiser. I may need to use force and you'd just get in my way.'

He got out and walked away and she hesitated, wondering whether to disobey him and follow. On the whole she decided he was probably right. If Gavin was drunk there might be a scene, whether she was there or not. Whatever methods Brodie used to get her brother out of that club it would be best is she didn't have to witness them.

Nervously, she watched in the driving-mirror as Brodie turned into the club entrance. It was stupid to feel guilty, as though in letting Brodie go there alone she was betraying Gavin. If she thought for an instant that her brother would come home if she asked him, she would have gone in there alone, but she couldn't get Gavin's bitter face out of her mind. Her brother was hurt and angry and off balance. He wouldn't listen to her, whatever she said.

She didn't have to wait very long. She heard the scuffle as Brodie pulled Gavin out of the door, heard her brother's voice raised in drunken fury. Gavin was swearing, using words that made her wince.

Brodie ignored what he was being called. He had Gavin's arm twisted up behind his back and he was propelling him along the road as fast as he could in the face of Gavin's violent struggles.

Donna got out shakily and opened the rear door of the car. Brodie thrust Gavin inside a moment later, and Donna got a look from her brother that made her face go white.

Brodie got behind the wheel and she sank back into

her seat. Gavin was wrenching at the door handle, but Brodie had already locked it electronically from the dashboard. Gavin was a prisoner. Realising that, he slumped back, fuming, and said nothing at all as Brodie drove back to the Cowley house along the motorway at a speed that made Donna clutch at the seat and swallow in sheer terror.

They pulled up on the drive and Brodie switched off the automatic door lock. Gavin stumbled out and into the house without a glance at either of them.

CHAPTER EIGHT

WHEN Donna visited her father next day, she was astonished to find that he was out of bed. She stopped and stared, her arms full of books and flowers, and James Cowley chuckled.

'Your eyes don't deceive you!'

'Do the staff know you're out of bed?' she asked, coming slowly towards him.

'Of course.' He was seated in an armchair, his thin body draped in a thick dressing-gown, maroon terry towelling, a newspaper clutched in one hand.

She bent and kissed his cheek. 'You look so much better! At this rate you'll be coming home soon.'

'In a week or so, they tell me. They think I'm making good progress. These days, they believe in getting you out of bed as soon as possible. Lying in bed for weeks just gives you bedsores and makes your recovery slower than it has to be.'

She laid the bunch of roses on his bed-table and showed him the detective stories she had brought him. 'Nice light reading for you—that will keep your mind active without making you agitated.'

He grimaced. 'I had a heart attack, not a brainstorm! My mind's fine.'

Donna looked around for another chair and saw one in the corner. She pulled it over next to him and sat down. 'How long have you been out of bed?' she asked.

'About five minutes before you arrived!' he said,

smiling at her. 'And I'll be put back as soon as you've gone. The general idea is to feed me back into ordinary life as fast as they can. They want my bed and don't scruple to tell me so.'

She laughed. 'It *is* a busy hospital!'

'As you say,' he agreed, nodding. 'Are those roses from the garden?'

'Yes, I thought you'd like to have your own roses instead of hothouse flowers.'

'Can I smell them?' he asked, and she got up and brought them over to him.

He bent his head and inhaled, closing his eyes, 'Ah, yes. Shop-bought flowers never seem to have a real scent. They're lovely, thank you, Donna. Did you pick them yourself?'

'Every one!' she said lightly. 'And got a thorn in my finger to prove it.' She held out her finger, smiling, and her father stared at the tiny dark red mark, then bent forward and kissed it.

Donna was utterly shaken. They both were, flushing and unable to look at each other. It was the first time her father had really shown affection since she was a very small girl. He pushed the roses into her hands in silence and she got up and replaced them on his bed-table.

'Where's Brodie today?' her father asked huskily.

'He went to work.' Donna sat down again, her eyes restlessly skating around the spotless, antiseptic room. 'He hadn't been since . . .' she broke off, not liking to say that Brodie hadn't been into the office since her father had his heart attack.

'Well, work must go on,' James Cowley said approvingly, nodding. 'Brodie's got a lot on his plate at the moment. I expect he's told you.'

He hadn't asked about Gavin, and she resented that on her brother's behalf and reminded her father edgily, 'Gavin would have come, but he isn't very well and we thought he'd better not visit you in case he was coming down with a cold.' It wasn't true, of course. Gavin hadn't emerged from his room by the time Donna was ready to leave for the hospital. No doubt he was sleeping off the excesses of last night. He had obviously been very drunk by the time Brodie caught up with him in the gambling club. It had been one in the morning by the time they got back to the house and Donna hadn't got to sleep until well past two. It hadn't been easy for her to get up that morning, and *she* hadn't been drunk, the night before. Gavin would probably have a head like a furred kettle this morning. She wasn't eager to see him again. He was going to be in one hell of a mood.

Her father frowned. 'I don't know what to do about Gavin, and that's the truth. I'd hoped he would get his act together sooner or later. He's not a fool. There's no reason why he shouldn't do well in the firm—but he just doesn't give his mind to it.'

Donna considered him wryly. How could you get it through to him that he was trying to force a square peg into a round hole?

'Did you ever dream about being a painter, Father?' she asked.

James Cowley looked amazed. 'A painter? An artist, you mean? Good God, no. Can't draw to save my life.'

'Gavin's a talented artist, did you know that?'

Her father gazed, brows heavy. 'Are you trying to tell me he wants to be a painter?'

'No,' she said, and he looked relieved.

'Well, thank heavens for that! You had me worried for a minute. I don't know anything about artists and I don't much care to know, either, A ramshackle lot—live in a hand-to-mouth way, morals don't mean a thing to them. I've always had a question mark against Gavin, he was a funny child, and he isn't much better now, either.'

'He wants to do something more with his life than work in an office,' Donna said gently. 'I think he may have real talent.'

'For what? Gambling? Drinking?' Her father was very flushed and his voice had an agitated note. She wished she had never started this discussion and drew back at once, smiling soothingly.

'I just meant that I think there's more to Gavin than you realise. He'll grow out of his wildness, I'm sure he will.'

Her father relaxed a little. 'I wish he was more like you,' he grunted. 'I'm proud of the way you've grown up. Going to France, getting a job, learning the language the way you did—I was angry at first, but as Brodie said, you needed to be independent for a while, find out what the world's like before you settled down. That might have been the right thing for Gavin to do. Maybe I was wrong, making him come into the firm. I'm human, I make mistakes, like anybody else. But for goodness' sake, Donna, he's nearly twenty-four! When is he going to stop acting like a fool?'

She had prickled at hearing Brodie quoted as an authority on what she did. So that was what Brodie had told her father, was it? It sounded remarkably like 'give her a little rope, then we'll pull her back to us'. A shiver ran down her back. Had Brodie always intended to come after her sooner or later? How had they kept an eye on what she did? Through Gavin? Her brother had visited her several times and she had written to him, but she hadn't communicated with either Brodie of her father and they hadn't been in touch with her. Had Brodie used the detective agency who had been watching her flat the night Gavin appeared in such a startling way? She wouldn't put it past him. It made her feel hunted to imagine him keeping a long-distance eye on her for the two years she had been in Paris.

'Talking about Paris,' she said flatly. 'I've got to go back there this weekend—a good friend of mine is getting married and I promised to be at her wedding. So I won't see you until I get back, Father. Next Tuesday, probably.'

'Is Brodie going with you?' he asked, frowning.

'No. He'll visit you. And so will Gavin. If I'm needed, they can get in touch with me quickly, don't worry, and I will be back, I promise.'

She wouldn't have gone if her father hadn't been so much better. Only that morning she had remembered that she must ring Alain Roche and explain that she couldn't come back that weekend, and then ring Marie-Louise to explain to her too, and wish her all the happiness in the world. But having seen how well James Cowley looked she decided she should go to Lyons. She could fly back from there on the Sunday, in fact, which would mean that she would only be away for two days.

She heard the bell signal the end of the visiting-period and got up to kiss her father. 'I'll try to be here on Monday, how's that?'

He smiled, nodding, but even when he looked

cheerful it made her wince to see how thin and frail he had become in the last two years. He had more colour today, it was true. His mouth no longer had that blue tinge nor was his face a deadly grey. But his neck resembled the neck of a tortoise, wrinkled and scaly, and his eyes were so sunken and tired, watering a little all the time.

When she got back to the house it was half past five because she had stopped in Saffron Walden to do some shopping and have tea in a little café close to the market square. Mrs Eyre was in the hall, polishing the table vigorously. She looked round, smiling.

'How's your father today?'

'Much better—out of bed and reading his newspaper!'

The housekeeper straightened her back. 'Well, that's marvellous news! Those doctors are wonderful the way they get him back on his feet. It was the same last time he had an attack. I really thought he'd never pull through that one, and Gavin was so upset—well, he would be, wouldn't he? It was all his father—but then he and his father have always quarrelled like dog and cat.' She gave Donna a rueful smile.

Thoughtfully, Donna asked, 'How did Gavin cause my father's attack?'

'I shouldn't have spoken out of turn, it's not my business,' said Mrs Eyre, looking agitated. 'It was just another of their arguments. Your father collapsed and was whisked off to hospital and Gavin didn't eat a thing for days. He's one of those who brood over everything, isn't he? A funny boy, he always was.'

Donna went up to her room, frowning. Was that why Gavin hadn't told her about their father's weak heart?

Guilt? A reluctance to talk about something he secretly felt he had caused?

She looked into his room, but it was empty, the door wide open and no sign of her brother. When had he got up? She turned back to ask Mrs Eyre where he was, but at that moment Brodie came out of his own room.

'Oh, you're back early,' she said stupidly, feeling her heart flip over. He had been gone by the time she got up that morning, and she had been expecting him back much later. She knew that office hours ended at five-thirty, and even if he left on time—which, being Brodie, he rarely did—she had worked out that it would take him several hours, at least, to get back here from the city during the rush hour.

'I left after lunch with a client,' he said. 'I'd managed to get through the backlog on my desk by midday, went off to lunch, then drove back to have a word with Gavin.'

'Where is he?'

'Oh, he's gone,' Brodie said coolly, walking back into his own room.

Donna followed, startled. 'Gone? What do you mean—gone?'

Brodie began unbuttoning his shirt. 'I'm just going to have a shower,' he said. 'It was damned hot driving back from London.'

'Where's Gavin?' Donna insisted, too agitated to notice at first what Brodie was doing.

'He's gone to the Midlands—he'll be away for a couple of days.' Brodie shrugged out of his shirt, and her nervous eyes flickered over his smooth, muscled shoulders, the deep tanned chest, the rough curls of black hair growing up the centre of it, and the flat midriff. Brodie might work in an office at a desk five days a week, but he had the powerful body of an athlete. In the confined space of the bedroom Donna became intensely conscious of that fact and backed towards the door and safety.

She swallowed an odd little lump in her throat. Her voice sounded rusty when it finally came out. 'Why?'

Brodie put a hand to the zip of his trousers. 'Can we talk later? I'm dying for that shower.'

Hot-cheeked, she spun on her heel and stood with her back to him, saying crossly, 'Just tell me why Gavin has gone to the Midlands. I thought we'd agreed that he wasn't to be left alone again until he saw this psychiatrist friend of yours?'

She heard the zip slide and hurriedly moved even further away, until she was actually in the doorway.

'Donna, you can't treat Gavin as if he were a child. If he's determined to gamble, nothing you can do will stop him. But he isn't alone, as it happens. One of our sales reps was going up to the Midlands this afternoon and Gavin went with him. George is level-headed, he knows Gavin's problem and he'll keep a fatherly eye on him. He has a son not much younger than Gavin. He can deal with it.'

She heard him stepping out of his trousers, and was about to leave when Brodie said, 'I've made an appointment for Gavin with a small private glass-works—if they like him, they might give him an apprenticeship. It's mainly stained glass they make, but it isn't a factory, it's an honest-to-God workshop, and he could learn far more there than he ever would at a technical school.'

Donna began to turn, then remembered that he was

probably naked, and stopped, her face very flushed.

'That's very good of you, was Gavin thrilled?' she stammered.

She heard Brodie move and tensed as his voice came from right behind her. 'He seemed excited, and he jumped at the chance to leave with George. His appointment is tomorrow morning and we'll know whether he's got the apprenticeship by tomorrow night.'

'Oh, good,' she said, shakily, anxious to get away from him, but as she began to walk off his hands caught her arms and held her back, pulling her against him.

'What are you doing?' she burst out thickly, a tremor running through her.

His mouth moved against her nape, his breathing stirred her hair. 'Is that all the thanks I get for going to so much trouble for your brother?'

'I thought you wanted a shower,' she muttered, fiercely aware of his thighs leaning against the back of her legs.

'It can wait,' he said, his hands sliding down her arms and closing on her waist, yet still holding her a prisoner.

'I've got a lot to do,' she protested, trying to break free.

His hands had wandered upwards, she felt his fingertips lightly brush her breasts and that galvanised her into a real struggle. Brodie let her go and laughed as she tore across the landing and slammed into her room.

She leaned on the door, breathless, angry, hot. How dared he maul her about like that when he was still having an affair with Christabel Clair? Whatever they had quarrelled about and whatever threat of leaving for

America she had made, Donna couldn't believe their affair was over. It had survived Christabel's infidelity—there must be a very serious bond between them. Perhaps Christabel had been unfaithful to him because Brodie had strayed first? That had never occurred to her until that moment—but now she thought back over the way he had acted ever since she saw him again in Paris and angrily bit her lip.

He had been flirting with her for days and he was good at it. She wouldn't find it hard to believe he meant it when he smiled at her like that. Yet she knew he still saw Christabel—which meant that Brodie wasn't to be trusted. He was deceptive; how many other woman had there been in his life? She had no idea, had she?

Was that why Christabel had been unfaithful to him? Donna didn't know her very well, but she could imagine that Christabel Clair was a jealous woman, capable of ruthless retaliation for a slight. Christabel wouldn't stand for any sort of treachery from him. She was tougher than Donna could ever be.

Brodie was a match for her, though. He was good at omitting facts, practising sleight of hand with the truth. After all, he had never told Donna about his relationship with Christabel. Not a syllable had passed his lips. Her father hadn't known he was engaged to anyone before he met Donna, had he?

She thought back bitterly to the first weeks after they met. She could have sworn that Brodie had nothing on his mind but work and herself. Who would have guessed that such a short time before they met he had been engaged to marry another woman and, presumably, in love?

They had met at a dinner-party in this house. Donna

had just finished college and was uncertain what to do next, but while she made up her mind she had taken a job with her father's newest factory in the personnel department. She had made it clear to her father that it was a temporary job. He had never taken much interest in her career stategy—she knew that that was because he didn't think girls needed careers. Her father had an old-fashioned view of women's rights. He simply thought that girls got married and stayed at home, unless their husband needed a little extra money for a year or two, in which case they worked until they could afford to have a baby.

Donna had always intended to have a career, in spite of that. Then she had met Brodie and her plans had dissolved. She knew, of course, almost at once, that her father was eager to pair them off. James Cowley made no secret of it. He pushed her at Brodie. She might have been furious if she hadn't been so attracted to Brodie anyway, right from that first meeting over dinner.

It was several months before Brodie first began to hint that they should get married, and by the time he did mention the idea Donna was head over heels in love. She couldn't remember a formal proposal. Brodie just talked casually about the future and seemed to take it for granted that it would be a future they shared. The moment when it crystallised for her was when he asked her where she wanted to live.

'Do you prefer the country? London would be more convenient,' he said lightly. She had breathlessly said either was fine.

A few days later as they walked past a Bond Street jeweller's Brodie had stopped and looked at rings in the window. 'Any stone you particularly fancy?'

She hadn't expected him to go down on his knees. That wasn't the modern way. Men today approached marriage practically; she was happy with Brodie's casual attitude.

She had been all too ready to fall in with whatever he suggested. Now she despised herself—she had been so easy to get! Brodie had lazily stretched out his hand and she had dropped into it like a ripe fruit.

Just at the moment when he was bitterly angry with Christabel he had met a girl who could offer him what Christabel couldn't—a solid gold future. He had begun chasing her with his eyes wide open while she had gone around in a besotted dream.

She bolted her door and sat on the bed, burning in self-contempt. What a fool she had been! And still was—even now that she knew just what sort of man he was, she couldn't get him out of her heart. Did he know she still cared?

If he didn't, it wasn't because she was so good at hiding her feelings. Angrily she faced the fact that she kept giving herself away. Every time he came near her she went weak at the knees. She was so jealous of Christabel that she couldn't stop herself from making a cheap, vicious remark, something she would never do in normal circumstances!

She got up reluctantly and went to her warbdrobe to find something to wear. If Gavin was away, she was going to be alone with Brodie, apart from Mrs Eyre, and the housekeeper stayed in her own flat once her work was done. Donna couldn't ask Mrs Eyre to join them. She could imagine the expression on the other woman's face if she did! Mrs Eyre thought they were lovers again, thanks to Brodie's insistence that they shouldn't tell her the truth.

He had an ulterior motive, of course. Donna wasn't fooled. She knew Brodie was plotting against her—but it wouldn't do him any good, because this time she wasn't going to be taken in by any of his smooth talk.

As she took a quick shower herself and changed she thought uneasily about the future. She couldn't leave her father alone. If Gavin did get a job in the Midlands she was going to have to give up her apartment in Paris and settle back at home again. That meant that Brodie would be around all the time. And that, in turn, meant trouble; she didn't need help in working that out.

Angry though she was with Brodie, she had to be grateful to him for helping Gavin to get this chance of an apprenticeship. No doubt Gavin had been over the moon about it. She was glad he was happy, but it left her such a problem! Could she bear to return to this battlefield on which she had been defeated so painfully once, knowing in her secret heart that her weapons were no more powerful this time, that Brodie had one overriding advantage—that she was still passionately in love with him?

When she had dressed in a simple green linen sheath with a stiff white collar and cuffs she sat in front of her dressing-table mirror staring grimly at her reflection.

She was such a fool. Brodie must know he had her in the palm of his hand. If she came back here, he would coolly take possession of her unless she could come up with some strategy for keeping him permanently at bay.

Brodie tapped on her door a short time later. 'Mrs Eyre would like to have dinner early tonight—she's visiting her sister, and wants to get away quickly.'

Donna went downstairs with him to eat the cold meal Mrs Eyre had put out—melon, followed by a salad with a platter of cold meat, and a gooseberry fool.

There were roses on the table from the garden—dark red ones with glowing hearts and petals like smooth skin.

'I gather your father will be coming home next week some time,' said Brodie. 'That's good news, isn't it? Mrs Eyre's already combing her recipe books for his favourite foods.'

Donna managed a faint smile, nodding. 'He looked so much better this afternoon—I hardly recognised him after the way he looked the first day.'

'If Gavin's going to be away, your father will be alone here,' Brodie said casually. 'Something will have to be done about that.'

She had hardly eaten a thing. She had no appetite. She felt like a mouse which had crept into an empty bottle left in a field—she was trapped and couldn't escape although she could see freedom all around her.

'You'll have to come home, Donna,' said Brodie in a soft voice, watching her intently, smiling.

She felt fever in her veins; a hectic iciness. He had her cornered and he knew it. She reached out a trembling hand and pulled a rose out of the vase and began methodically shredding it; crimson petal by crimson petal falling from her fingers in a passionate rain.

She couldn't answer, although she had already decided to do just that. Her eyes stared fixedly at the tumbling petals and Brodie watched her.

'Your father can't live alone, not in his state of health. It's either you or Gavin, Donna. I can't make you come home, but if you don't, Gavin won't get his chance to escape.'

Was that why he had gone to so much trouble to get Gavin an apprenticeship in the Midlands? Only then did it occur to her that Brodie might have done that deliberately, with the intention of forcing her back from France. He had a convoluted mind; it wasn't easy to follow the twists and turns of it even when you knew the motives propelling him.

It was at that instant that she decided to leave for Paris first thing in the morning without telling Brodie she was going. She had intended to tell him and Mrs Eyre this evening, but now she saw that if she was ever to establish her own right to make a decision, if she was ever to defy his attempt to manipulate and control her, she must start at once. Now, tonight, she must make a private declaration of independence.

She was going to Paris because she chose to—she was going on to Lyons with her friends because she chose to. If Brodie knew she meant to go, he would try to stop her. She knew that with utter certainty. He would threaten, cajole, persuade—somehow he would find a way of stopping her if he could.

So she wouldn't give him the chance to do any of that. She would take a leaf out of his book—if he could be cunning and deceitful, so could she! She would tell him she had a headache, in a minute, and go up to bed early. Of course, he wouldn't believe a word of it. He would smile sarcastically and think she was running away because she was so scared of being alone with him. But he wouldn't be able to stop her and because he was so confident of winning in the end he would probably let her go, and once she was safely in her room with the door locked she would quietly pack a few things.

Tomorrow when he had gone to the office she would get Mrs Eyre to drive her to the railway station and she would get the first possible plane to Paris.

CHAPTER NINE

MARIE-LOUISE didn't look radiant—she looked positively incandescent, thought Donna, as she watched her friend at the wedding reception, going from group to group in the hotel ballroom, kissing them in the French manner, once on each cheek for distant relatives, twice on each cheek for close friends and three times on each cheek when she hugged her grandmother, who had lent Marie-Louise the soft, goldy-white veil she wore. It was more than two hundred years old, that lace, and had been made by one of Marie-Louise's family here in Lyons. No doubt it had been pure white when it was first made, but time had conferred on it a gentle colour change—it was now a yellowing ivory. Among its folds gleamed pearls and tiny white roses, the coronet holding it in place.

The wedding had been very long and very beautiful; a sung mass with a choir hidden somewhere and a haunting echo of their voices coming back from the high roof of the mediaeval church. Looking upwards, Donna had seen angel faces among the dark wooden beams, carved gilded cherubs flying over their heads. The sun had shone through ancient stained glass, colouring the faces of the congregation. Marie-Louise's voice had sounded unfamiliar, husky, uncertain, but there was nothing unsure about her now—she blazed with happiness.

'You look wistful, *chérie*,' remarked Alain, leaning

over to smile at Donna.

'Sorry, do I?' She had been trying to smile for hours now. It wasn't easy because she envied Marie-Louise so much. It must be wonderful to be so secure in your love; to feel no doubts, no anxieties, no pangs of jealousy.

'Would you like to be getting married?'

'Is that a proposal?'

Alain laughed, putting up both hands in Gallic horror. 'Ah, no, *chérie*! I am not the marrying type. But you, I think, are.' His glinting eyes watched her thoughtfully. 'Yes, I think so.'

'Most people are, sooner or later,' shrugged Donna.

'This is true, but I am not most people,' Alain said with grateful fervour.

An hour later they danced together and almost bumped into Marie-Louise and her husband as Alain swirled Donna around, the full skirts of her strawberry-pink dress flying up in rustling layers.

'Having a good time?' Marie-Louise asked over her husband's shoulder, winking.

'Terrific!'

It was odd, but Donna already felt that Marie-Louise was different—from now on their lives would be totally separated, they might keep in touch, but it would never be the same again. Marie-Louise would have other preoccupations, other friends, other things on her mind. A wedding was the end as well as a beginning; one of the great divides of life.

They had a chance for a talk a little later when Marie-Louise and Jean-Paul stopped dancing and came to sit at the same table. Marie-Louise sent Alain off to dance with another girl in the party and chased her new husband away, smiling at him.

'Go and talk to your mother! She is all alone. I want to talk to Donna.'

Jean-Paul kissed her nose. 'Okay, *mignonne*! Don't forget, we leave in half an hour!'

'As if I would!'

'When women start talking they forget everything!' Jean-Paul grinned and went off, however, and Marie-Louise smoothed back her veil with a tender hand.

'Marriage is exhausting—it will take me a month to get over it. I don't know whether I'm on my head or my heels—I seem to have been rushing about for days now.'

'You look good on it,' Donna said affectionately, smiling back at her. 'It obviously suits you.'

Her friend laughed. 'Yes, I think so.' Her face became a little more serious. 'But tell me, *chérie*—what is this about your father being very ill? Alain told me a while ago. I'd no idea! Is it very serious?'

'He's recovering a little, but he has a weak heart,' Donna answered soberly, and told her about the events of the past week. 'I thought for a while that I wouldn't get to your wedding, in fact, but he was so much better that I thought I would risk it. I left the name and phone number of the hotel here with the hospital and my father's housekeeper so that if anything did happen they could reach me quickly, but in any case I've decided to fly back early tomorrow morning. I'm sorry to miss the fun Alain and the others are organising for tomorrow, but I think I ought to get back.'

Marie-Louise nodded. 'Of course. You must be very worried. It was good of you to come all this way when you had so much on your mind.' She leaned over and kissed Donna lightly on both cheeks. 'Thank you for the lovely silver fruit bowl. We will cherish it.'

'And you'll keep in touch?'

'Without fail.' Marie-Louise looked at her thoughtfully. 'And what will you do now? You won't stay in Paris, if your father is so ill?'

'No, I think I'll have to go home to live,' Donna agreed, sighing.

'It is a pity, I know how much you enjoyed Paris— but family is family.'

Donna smiled ruefully. 'How true!'

She didn't confide in Marie-Louise all the other problems on her mind. It wasn't something she wanted to talk about, and it wasn't the time or place for such confidences, anyway.

Marie-Louise eyes twinkled. 'Alain will be very disappointed. He's always fancied you and he probably thought he had a chance to get you alone for a while!'

Donna laughed. 'Too bad for Alain! He'll survive. There are plenty of other fish in the sea for Alain.'

The party continued for a long time after the bridal couple had left on their honeymoon. The band went on playing, the dancers went on dancing, people went on drinking and talking at the tables for some hours until gradually they drifted away in groups of two or three or more, saying goodbye to Marie-Louise's parents before they slipped away.

'I think we ought to go,' Donna murmured to Alain, glancing at her watch and seeing that it was gone ten o'clock. 'If I'm to fly back to London tomorrow, I ought to get to bed quite early.'

He made a wry face. 'The night's still young! I thought we'd go on to dance somewhere after we left here.'

The others in the group nodded cheerfully. 'Good idea! Let's do that!'

'I can't,' said Donna.

They tried to persuade her for a few more minutes. 'We may not see you for a long time! One last evening—come on, Donna!'

'Weddings depress me,' Alain said mournfully, looking quite lugubrious, his eyes dark circles in his ugly-attractive face. 'I need cheering up!'

Donna laughed at him. 'I'm sure someone will do that! One of your little flies!'

Their friends rocked with laughter. 'Mr Frog and his little flies,' they chorused. 'Yes, one will come buzzing around you, Alain!'

He gazed coaxingly at Donna. 'But I want you to come—just tonight, one evening together, just us, Donna.'

'I'd have loved to, but I can't, Alain, not tonight. Some other time we'll have dinner together and talk or whatever.' His friends hooted softly, but she ignored them, concentrating on Alain's reproachful expression. 'It's been such a scramble to get here for the wedding and I'm dead on my feet. I must get some sleep tonight.'

He shrugged resignation. 'Okay—but I'll see you back to the hotel.' He looked at the others, grinning at their amused expressions. 'You can go on to the disco club. I'll find you there later.'

'Much later?' they enquired wickedly.

Donna gave them a dry, irritated look. She knew what they were thinking—that Alain would stay with her for a few hours. If that was what Alain had in mind he could think again!

On the way back to the hotel, though, she realised

Alain had no motive in taking her back there except to make sure she arrived carefully. As soon as they were alone his manner lapsed into ordinary friendliness. His persistence with her had been purely for the benefit of his friends—and his own reputation.

It must be a bore having to live up to that, she thought. Poor Alain; did he feel tired every time he saw a woman?

With her, at least, he could talk of other things—books, plays, films. The subject of sex didn't enter into their murmured conversation.

When they got to the hotel, Alain came with her in the lift up to the floor on which they both had rooms. Outside her room he watched her unlock the door and switch on the light, then kissed her on both cheeks, holding her shoulders, as if she were a soldier getting a medal for bravery and he were a general.

'Don't forget us, *chérie*. I'm going to miss you—you'll keep in touch? You'll write now and then?'

She nodded, smiling up at him. 'Of course, if you'll write back.'

'I don't have your home address,' he said. 'Will you give it to me tonight—if you don't remember to write to me I can remind you!'

She laughed and opened her bag to find a pencil and paper. Alain came into the room and closed the door with his foot; the latch didn't click and she had no worries that he might be planning to stay. He stood politely watching her begin to scribble down her home address.

His friends would never believe that their relationship was platonic! She might well have smiled cynically at the notion if she had been told that Alain's friendship with any other woman was purely asexual. The trouble with men was that their ego formed their idea of themselves and everyone else accepted that self-image. Alain wanted to have a reputation as a great lover—or had done when he was younger. Now he was bored with it but couldn't shake it off. It had once been a halo round his head—now it was a millstone round his neck. Poor Alain!

She handed him the piece of paper and he glanced at the address before folding it and sliding it into his wallet.

'Have a safe trip back to England tomorrow,' he said, turning to the door. '*Au revoir, petite*. I hope your father is much better when you get home.'

The hotel was half empty, as they had noticed when they arrived, and now it was very still and silent, presumably all the other guests were either out enjoying themselves or fast asleep, so they kept their voices down discreetly, murmuring to each other in soft French.

'Goodnight, Alain.' said Donna, kissing his cheek. 'Have a good time tonight.'

He grimaced. 'I don't know why I do it.' The door stood partially open now. He turned to go saying, 'But I suppose I must join the others or they'll think the worst.' His eyes held a faint amusement. He took hold of the door. 'Now you can get to bed,' he said teasingly, and at that second someone pushed against the door violently and Alain tumbled backwards, taking Donna with him. Instinct made her grab at him to save herself falling. Alain collided with the wall of her room, a stunned expression on his sallow face. He threw his arms round her, grunting as if winded.

'Are you okay, *chérie?*'

'What . . .' she began, looking round at the door.

'Some drunk, I suppose,' Alain said in French, his tone disgusted.

Donna was staring at the man framed in the doorway; her face first white, then scalding red.

'I'll deal with him,' Alain assured her, gently shifting her to one side so that he could square up to Brodie Fox. He had seen him before, but he didn't appear to have recognised him this time.

Donna couldn't move or speak; she was too horrified. What was Brodie doing here?

'*M'sieur,* please leave before I call the hotel security,' said Alain in clipped French.

'I want to talk to you,' Brodie told Donna in English that had icicles on it.

Alain's head swung back to her, brows rising. '*Chérie.* You know him?'

Flushed, she began to say, 'Yes, he . . .'

'Get your boy-friend out of here before I spoil his face!' Brodie cut across her stammered explanation.

Alain's eyes narrowed on his face. 'I've seen him before, I think? Yes? In Paris at the Ritz, that was the man you were dining with?'

Half angry, half upset, Donna said, 'I'm sorry, Alain—you'd better go, I'll have to talk to him.'

He gave one of his wry little shrugs. 'Are you sure you want to, *chérie?*'

'Whether she wants to or not, she's going to,' Brodie said in Alain's own tongue, investing the French with considerable bite.

Alain considered him without seeming very impressed. 'He looks rather bad-tempered,' he said to

Donna as if Brodie couldn't understand him, in spite of the fact that he must now realise that Brodie did.

'You had better believe it,' grated Brodie through his teeth, Then he turned on Donna with a violence that made her jump. 'Get him out of here before *I* do!'

'*M'sieur* your manners leave much to be desired,' Alain said with enormous dignity, drawing himself up to his full height but completely failing to look any more impressive beside Brodie's six feet of muscled power.

'I'm not wasting any more time on him,' Brodie said, lip curling, taking a long stride towards him.

Donna leapt between them as Alain immediately tensed to meet whatever Brodie meant to do.

'That's enough! How dare you come bursting in here, throwing your weight around?'

'I am not scared of him, *chérie*,' Alain told her, dancing on his toes with his fists up. 'Let him try to hit me! I learnt to box at school.'

'No, I don't want any fighting in here—Alain, you'd better go now. Don't worry about me, I can handle him.' She hoped her voice sounded a little more confident than she felt. She suspected it didn't, from the searching look she got from Alain.

'You think so? It doesn't look like it to me! But if that's what you want, I'll be in my own room across the corridor—if you need me, you only have to call.'

Brodie was listening, his brows black and drawn above his glittering eyes. Donna ignored him and smiled waveringly at Alain.

'Thank you. I'll remember.'

Alain nodded and gave Brodie a long stare. '*M'sieur*, upset Donna and you'll have me to deal with.'

Brodie didn't bother to answer him; he merely

snarled wordlessly, holding the door open in a very pointed fashion. Alain went out, bristling, and Brodie slammed the door after him.

'How dare you behave like this to a friend of mine?' Donna burst out, trembling with anger.

'Friend?' Brodie laughed shortly.

'What are you doing in Lyons, anyway? You must have followed me here.' She was only just beginning to think clearly and a pang of alarm flashed across her face. 'My father . . .?'

'He's still holding his own—not that that bothers you much, or you wouldn't have come over here to meet your boy-friend!'

'Don't shout at me!' said Donna coldly, eyeing him with resentment. It was a relief to know that her father wasn't any worse, but once she had taken that in she found her mind filling with other, just as violent, feelings. Who did Brodie think he was? What made him believe he had the right to put her actions under some sort of moral microscope? She remembered Christabel Clair with mounting fury and bitter distate—Brodie was a hypocrite. If he thought he could walk in here and sit in judgement on her he was quite wrong.

'How could you do it?' Brodie demanded, looking at her as though he couldn't believe his eyes. 'You came here with him for the weekend—is he your lover?'

'Mind your own business!'

'It is my business,' Brodie ground out almost without unclenching his teeth.

'Oh, no, it isn't!'

'Damn you, I tell you it is!' shouted Brodie, making her uneasily conscious of the stillness of the hotel around them. Alain would have heard that from his room. She didn't want him coming back. Brodie was in the sort of mood where he might do anything, and Donna didn't want to find herself being turned out of the hotel in the middle of the night, or being taken off to the Lyons police station in a pair of handcuffs.

'Be quiet!' she hissed. 'How dare you come into my room kicking up a scene like this! I didn't ask you in here and I don't want you anywhere near me, so get out!'

He took a step closer and bent, his face a threat even though he didn't actually touch her.

Have you slept with that Frenchman?'

Scarlet, Donna slapped his face.

Brodie's head went back with the impact, a hot brand appearing on his cheek where she had made contact. For a second Donna thought he was going to hit her back, then he took hold of her shoulders and shook her violently.

'That's no answer! Tell me the truth!'

'It's all the answer you're going to get! What right do you think you have to question me about my private life? You haven't told me anything about yours, have you? And mine is a damn sight less eventful that yours!'

He didn't let go of her, ignoring her furious struggle to get free.

'I'm trying not to lose my temper!' he said, and she laughed in angry disbelief at this fantastic statement.

'What?'

'But I want the truth,' Brodie went on, ignoring that too. He appeared to be breathing as if he had just done an hour's jogging. 'Answer me!'

'Why should I?' Donna threw back, and that seemed

to be a strategic mistake, like pouring petrol on a fire, because Brodie broke out even more angrily.

'How could you let him come anywhere near you?' His voice thickened with rage; he shook her with such force that her hair flew all over the place; covering her eyes. 'I'd like to kill you!'

Donna peered at him throuh the strands of hair, her stomach clenching at the way he said that. If she hadn't known what a plausible liar and hypocrite he was, she might almost have believed he meant that.

'Donna,' he said huskily, the faintest softening in his voice. 'You're torturing me—tell me the truth. Why did you come here to meet that fellow? You aren't in love with him, you can't be.'

'Why can't I?' she asked rhetorically. 'Alain's a nice man.'

Brodie made a grating, grinding noise with his teeth.

'A lot of women are in love with Alain,' said Donna defiantly.

'You must be joking! That ugly little creep?'

'He has to fend them off with judo,' Donna said with an angry triumph.

Brodie's expression was incredulous. 'I don't believe it—but even if it's true, I can't believe that *you* fancy him.'

'Why shouldn't I?'

'Because . . .' Brodie's voice broke off, deepening. 'You know very well why, Donna. You belong to me.'

She went white, shaking. 'Oh, no, I don't. I hate the very sight of you.'

'No,' he said fiercely. His hands flew up to frame her face. He bent and kissed her mouth with a passion that made her head spin, his lips hot and insistent, refusing to let her pull away until her body weakened and her own emotions undermined her resistance. Her eyes closed and her fingers gripped his shoulders, her head sinking back under the force of his kiss.

When Brodie lifted his head again she was dizzy and sick with self-contempt. She had been so determined not to let him get to her this time. She knew only too well what lay behind his pursuit of her to France, why he was so angry at the very idea that she should find another man attractive. Brodie didn't care whether she slept with Alain or not—all that worried him was his own future with her father's firm if he couldn't persuade her to marry him. He wanted her half of the family shares, her voting power in the company. He didn't want her personally at all. He never had—it had always been Christabel he really loved, if he could love anyone.

He looked down at her, a smile curving his mouth—a smile of complacency, triumph, self-congratulation, she thought, hating him. His eyes had a drowsy excitement, his face was darkly flushed—if she hadn't known better she might have believed that Brodie was in the grip of emotions as strong as her own.

But the truth was that Brodie had forced her to betray herself, and he was cock-a-hoop about it.

'We'll get married right away, before your father comes out of hospital. He couldn't stand the excitement of wedding arrangements, it would be much wiser to make his mistake the real thing without bothering to tell him.'

Donna went ice-cold, swallowing on a hard lump in her throat. 'No!' she whispered. He thought he had won, didn't he? But he was going to find how wrong he was! For once in his all-conquering career, Brodie Fox was going to suffer a defeat—and at her hands!

He looked at her mockingly. 'Yes, Donna,' he said softly, eyes gleaming with total assurance. 'Don't waste any more of our time with arguing.'

'You really must think I'm stupid!' she broke out. 'Do you think I've forgotten Christabel Clair? I haven't. I'm not sharing you with her, any more than she wants to share you with me. You'd better get it into your head, Brodie! You're never going to marry me!'

CHAPTER TEN

BRODIE stared at her attentively. 'Christabel?' he echoed.

Don't pretend you don't know what I mean! You are still having an affair with her—you admitted it the other day. She rang you and you went out to meet her and didn't come back all night, and when I told you I knew you didn't even deny it!'

'I told you I was out most of the night, I didn't say I'd been with Christabel.'

'It was Christabel who rang you. I talked to her myself—I know it was her.'

He walked over to a chair and sat down, stretching his long legs with an impatient sigh. 'Sit down, Donna.'

'I'm not . . .'

'Sit down!' His voice cracked like a whip and she stiffened in shock and affront. But perhaps it might be wiser to humour him this once because he was frowning in a way which alarmed her, and anyway, she wanted to hear his explanation. She had no intention of believing a word of it. She knew what a liar and a cheat he was. But she might as well listen. Calmly, with dignity, she walked to the bed and sat down on the furthest end of it, far enough away from him to be able to move fast if he took a step in her direction. A bed wasn't the safest place to be when you were alone with Brodie Fox.

He watched her, frowning. 'When I told you why I broke off my engagement to Christabel in the first place, there was one important piece I left out of my story.'

She threw a barbed look at him. 'I noticed.'

'Don't interrupt!' he snapped. 'You want to hear the whole story—I'm going to tell you the whole story, but I don't want you interrupting every two seconds.' He ran a hand over his dark hair. 'Where was I? Oh, yes, I didn't tell you the name of the man Christabel had an affair with—you know him and . . .'

'I know him?' Her voice died away as Brodie fixed a menacing glitter on her.

'What did I just tell you? You've thrown me off my track again. You can say whatever you like when I've finished telling you, but until then for heaven's sake, shut up!'

'No need to shout!' she muttered. 'Well, go on!'

'Thank you,' he said through his teeth. 'I didn't want the story getting around for his wife's sake—and he has a couple of kids! I'd promised him I wouldn't tell a living soul. Give me your word you won't tell anyone, Donna.'

'I promise I won't,' she said frowning.

He watched her uncertainly, then said, 'It was Tom Reed.'

Her jaw dropped. *'Tom?'* She couldn't believe it. Tom's wife, Jinny, was so pretty, a charming girl with kind, direct eyes and a lovely smile. They had two children and had always seemed so happy. Donna had always preferred Jinny to Tom who was slightly boring; a rather pompous man with an inflated idea of his own importance, interested in nothing but his own success and his own view of the world, it had seemd to her. Donna found it difficult to believe that Tom Reed would have an affair with anyone, let alone Christabel. He simply wasn't the type. He didn't seem to Donna to have the imagination to be unfaithful.

'I told you I broke his nose—didn't you notice Tom's nose is out of true? It never set properly.'

She suddenly realised that she *had* noticed Tom's nose, although she had never connected Tom with the man Brodie had had a fight with over Christabel. At that party, in Tom's house, she had several times caught sight of his nose and had wondered if he had broken it playing rugger the way a friend of Gavin's had. It had looked like that—a bump on the end of it and a distinct twist to the right.

'I did wonder how he'd broken his nose,' she said slowly. 'I decided it was probably rugger.'

'No, it was me,' said Brodie with a sort of grim satisfaction.

'That doesn't prove anything,' Donna threw at him. 'You can tell me any story you like—how do I know it's the truth? For all I know Tom Reed did break his nose playing rugger and barely knows Christabel.' She fixed Brodie with a cynical smile. 'If he was the man, why did you see so much of him once you knew? I didn't pick up any hint that you had anything against him. At the time, I thought he was your best friend.'

'He had been,' Brodie told her curtly. 'I stood godfather to his little boy. I'm fond of Jinny, she's a very nice girl. After I found out about Tom and Christabel, I had an almightly row with him, as I told you. I didn't see him for weeks, but we do business together, we belong to the same clubs—if I played golf, I'd see Tom. If I went for a drink, I'd see him at the bar. I couldn't just cut him off without a lot of gossip and without hurting Jinny's feelings. Gradually it dawned on me that it was Christabel who was to blame, not Tom. He isn't the type to wreck his marriage over another woman, he loves his kids. We met and had a few drinks and he swore he'd never see Christabel again, it was over, so . . .' He shrugged at her.

Donna stared. 'But she was at Tom's and Jinny's party!'

Brodie fixed hard eyes on her. 'And that's where you met her, isn't it?'

She nodded.

'Tom told me that the other night.' His smile was grim. 'The night Christabel rang urgently needing to talk to me—she needed my help. Tom had been at her place that evening and had collapsed. He was rambling, delirious, she couldn't get any sense out of him and he obviously couldn't drive himself home. Christabel thought he might be dying—she didn't know what to do. I went there and found Tom with a raging temperature, so I put him in my car, wrapped in a blanket. He was stark naked—Christabel hadn't been able to get his clothes back on him. So I took Tom to a hospital, told them he'd collapsed in the bath at the club after playing squash. I think they believed it—but it was Jinny I wanted to convince, of course. I had to make the story convincing. I stayed long enough at the hospital to find out that Tom had pneumonia, a viral kind, they said. Comes on suddenly with a gallop, he'd probably caught it from someone. They said he was very ill indeed and might have pleurisy. They were scathing about people playing sports when they are obviously ill. Once I knew Tom wasn't in immediate danger, I drove to his house to see Jinny. I thought I ought to be there when she heard the news. She was quite calm, actually, but she wanted to go to Tom, she insisted on staying at the hospital all night. Her mother had to drive over from the other side of London, so I said I'd stay in the house until the mother arrived so that Jinny could go at once. The mother didn't get there until gone midnight, and by the time I got back to your house it was nearly three.'

Donna believed the story. It was too circumstantial to be invented—it was easy anough to check, after all. There were too many other people involved for it to be a lie—he couldn't get the hospital to back him up in a lie, or Jinny's mother.

'So Tom hadn't stopped seeing Christabel,' she said slowly.

Brodie's face was angry. 'He'd lied to me. He didn't know what he was saying the night he collapsed, he kept on talking in this funny rambling way, and I found out a lot of things—for instance, how you came to meet Christabel. She engineered that, twisted Tom's arm to get him to invite her. It was the last thing he wanted to do—he was terrified of Jinny finding out what was going on. But Christabel blackmailed him into letting her come to his party—she suggested that Tom told Jinny she was one of his firm's clients. Jinny was rather amused to hear that a top model was investing with Tom's help. It didn't dawn on her that there was any more to it, of course. As far as Jinny knew, she had the perfect marriage.'

Donna winced at the bite of his voice. 'Poor Jinny!'

'Yes.' Brodie got up from the chair and came over towards her. Donna was suddenly nervous of him again. She didn't like the look in his eyes.

'That night was the first time I'd seen Christabel in two years,' Brodie told her in a crisp, insistent tone, sitting down next to her on the bed.

Donna shrank back against the pillows. 'And all that time Tom must have been going on with the affair. How could he do that to Jinny?' Although she was nervous about having Brodie so close to her, she was angry, too. If Jinny found out how would she feel?

'How could he do that?' she said again.

'God knows,' Brodie said tersely. 'I was so angry I almost felt like telling Jinny, smashing the whole thing wide open. She doesn't deserve a guy like Tom. I felt pretty furious with him about the way he'd lied to me, but I knew Jinny would be totally shattered. I couldn't tell her. Maybe I should have done, I don't know—all I do know is, I couldn't.'

'Oh, no, you couldn't!' Donna agreed. 'But it doesn't seem fair that he should get away with it. Years of lying and cheating! And he knew Christabel had deliberately gone out of her way to break up our . . .' She stopped, eyes meeting Brodie's.

'Yes,' he said softly, dangerously. 'I finally found out from Tom that I had him and Christabel to thank for that. It seemed to be on his conscience, he kept talking about it while he was delirious. To do him justice, I think Tom's so obsessed with Christabel that she can make him jump through hoops. He's such a very ordinary fellow; not too bright in some ways, a careful plodder more than a genius. He's always done the right things all his life. Worked hard, been a good husband and father, a pillar of the community—in the beginning I think he had a little fling with Christabel out of sheer boredom. Just for once he wanted to live dangerously. And then he got hooked. He couldn't give her up. I don't know if I'd call it love; it's too feverish for that. Tom's addicted, that's all.'

He looked at her, and Donna felt suddenly very uneasy. There was a warning glitter in his eyes.

She looked away, swallowing, 'You'd better go—it's very late and I have to get up in the morning to fly back to London.'

'I've told you the truth. I could use a little truth from you in return,' said Brodie, ignoring that. 'What's going on between you and that Frenchman?'

She kept her eyes down. 'We're friends, that's all.'

'Just good friends?' he sounded sarcastic; he obviously didn't believe her.

She looked up defiantly. 'That's all! We aren't here alone—we came in a party of eight. A friend of ours got married here today, we've been at the reception. The others went out dancing afterwards and Alain wanted me to go, but I said I had to get an early night so he saw me back to the hotel. He was going to join the others later.'

'And he doesn't fancy you?' drawled Brodie disbelievingly.

'Alain has a different woman every day of the week. He has incredible sex appeal, but he's rather tired of it, poor Alain. I'm a friend, there's never been anything else between us.'

'He has sex appeal?' Brodie's brows rose in dark arches. 'You're kidding!'

'You aren't a woman!' Donna said drily.

'That's true,' he murmured, smiling. 'Want me to prove it?'

She shifted further away. 'I wish you'd get off my bed! And leave!'

'We still have a few things to discuss,' he said coolly without budging.

'We don't have anything to discuss!'

'Why didn't you tell me that you were coming to Lyons to a friend's wedding? Why did you just leave?'

'I told my father and Mrs Eyre—and left my address here in case of emergency!'

'You didn't tell me,' he underlined with a flick of those cool eyes. 'Why, Donna?'

'Why should I? I don't have to tell you anything! I'm a free agent. I can come and go as I choose!' He might have convinced her that he wasn't having an affair with Christabel, but she still didn't believe he wanted to marry her because he loved her. He wanted her father's firm and she was the quickest way to get it.

'You wanted to make me jealous!' he accused.

Her face was hot. 'I didn't! I didn't tell you where I was going because I thought you might try to stop me.'

'You knew I wouldn't like the idea of you joining that Frenchman at Lyons for a weekend, you mean!'

'I mean that I didn't want all the hassle I knew I'd get if I told you I was coming back to France.'

'It comes to the same thing. You knew I wouldn't be too happy at the idea of you spending time with another man!'

'I've been doing that for the past two years and you haven't known anything about it!'

His face stiffened. 'Has there been anyone else, Donna?'

She couldn't quite meet the probe of his eyes. She didn't want to admit that there hadn't; that would give him too much to crow about.

He suddenly caught her chin in one hand and tipped her head back to make her look at him.

'I love you, Donna,' he said huskily.

She felt a deep, fierce pain inside her chest. 'Don't lie to me! You want my father's firm, not me!'

'I've *got* your father's firm,' he said harshly.

Donna's body jerked in shock. She stared at him, unable to ask what he meant. His face was grim and taut; all angles, his jaw clenched, his mouth hard, his eyes fixed on her.

'I've had it for nearly three years,' he said shortly. 'I bought a number of shares before I joined the firm. I've been adding to them since and when I realised I wanted to marry you I suggested that your father sell me enough shares to give me control. There was never any question of Gavin being able to run the company. Not merely because his heart isn't in it, but because he simply hasn't got the right sort of mind. Gavin's no businessman—your father knew that. When I told him I was going to marry you, he agreed to sell the block of shares you were going to inherit anyway. He didn't see why I was doing it until I pointed out that I didn't want anyone to think I was marrying you to get those shares.'

She bit her lower lip, very shaky. 'Why didn't you tell me?'

'I would have done—those shares were going to be my wedding present,' he said shortly.

Donna closed her eyes. 'Oh, Brodie, you fool!'

'Yes, I must have been a fool to think you'd trust me,' he said with a dry anger. 'I believed you loved me enough to marry me without knowing for certain that I didn't want the firm. You never seemed to doubt it until you met Christabel. Everything was fine until then, but out of that clear blue sky you hit me like a hurricane and before I knew what was happening you'd gone.'

'But you didn't come after me, explain.'

'Explain what? I didn't know you'd found out about Christabel. You didn't tell me why you suddenly turned against me, remember. You just told me you hated the sight of me and left, and after the things you said about me I was in such a state of shock that it was weeks before I started thinking clearly.'

'But you must have wondered.'

'Of course I damned well wondered! I went crazy trying to work out what had gone wrong between us. Your father and I talked it over and he said he thought you were probably just too young to think of marriage yet. He said I should leave you alone for a year or so, give you time to have some fun, experiment a little.' He paused, looking at her fixedly. 'Did you?'

'In some ways,' she said, looking down.

'What ways?' His voice thickened and she glanced through her lashes at him.

'I learnt a lot of French, discovered how to cook, got to know Paris very well,' she shrugged casually, knowing she was annoying him.

'Stop playing games! You know what I meant!' he erupted, moving closer and watching her like a cat at a mousehole. 'Has there been anyone else?'

'No,' she said, half smiling.

'It isn't funny,' Brodie gritted fiercely, gripping her shoulders. 'Don't laugh at me, damn you!'

'Two years is a long time to wait,' she said, feeling the tension of his fingers with a certain satisfaction. 'Why didn't you come to Paris to find me?'

'Frankly, because there hadn't been a sign from you,' he told her in brusque impatience. 'I have my pride. I wasn't chasing you if you really couldn't care less. I thought if you cared, you'd come home sooner or later and then I'd be able to tell.'

'Tell what?'

He shook her briefly. 'Tell whether I'd be wasting my time to try again,' he said curtly. 'When your father started having these heart attacks I wanted to get in touch, but he didn't want you brought back
for that, and none of them was grave enough to warrant ignoring what he said. If they had become really serious, I would have felt I had to disobey him. It wasn't until Gavin bolted and I guessed he'd gone to you that I followed him, and had a good excuse for seeing you.'

Donna looked teasingly through her lashes. 'Excuse? You felt you needed one?'

'Of course I did! I didn't want you thinking I was

following you to Paris because I couldn't live without you.'

'You're an idiot,' she said, slipping her arms round his neck.

He looked down into her half-closed, smiling eyes. 'I am?'

'How was I ever to know you really did love me if you stayed away from me?'

'There is that,' he accepted drily, his arms round her waist, pulling her closer. 'But it works both ways. How was I to know how you felt when you lived it up in Paris and seemed to have forgotten I existed?'

'I hadn't,' she said softly, staring at the passionate curve of his mouth.

'No?' His mouth came closer.

'I tried, but I couldn't,' she whispered as it touched her.

'Darling,' muttered Brodie, kissing her with a hunger that shook her to the depths. He pulled her down on the bed, holding her so tightly it wasn't easy to breathe. 'I love you so much,' he said, kissing her neck. 'I can't begin to tell you! I wondered if I'd still feel the same when I saw you again—two years is a long time, as you said, and although I hadn't forgotten you I wondered if I loved what I remembered rather than the real girl. Then I saw you in the doorway of that apartment and I knew it was all as real as the floor under my feet.'

She laughed, touching his cheek tenderly with one hand. 'Brodie, I don't believe it—you're a romantic under all the steel and flint. And I thought you were just a businessman!'

'Business is romantic,' he said, grinning. 'Gavin's too young and crazy to realise how romantic it is to make windows for people's houses, but you're no fool, Donna. You must understand! Every time I drive past a new housing estate I look at all those gleaming new windows and think . . . we made some of that!'

She kissed him. 'No wonder my father thinks the sun shines out of you! You think just like him!'

He stroked her hair, his face sober. 'Will you marry me, Donna?'

'Yes, please,' she said, throwing pretence to the winds.

He kissed her again, slowly, deeply. 'I'll make you happy.'

'We'll make each other happy,' she corrected, and Brodie laughed.

'Yes, that's what I meant. One thing, though, if Gavin does take this job in the Midlands your father will be alone in that damn great house.'

'I'd forgotten Gavin's interview—how did it go?' she asked.

'They seemed to like him, and he certainly flipped over the work they're doing. They offered him the apprenticeship and he has to let them know Monday. The one problem bothering him was your father.' Brodie looked uncertainly at her. 'How do you feel about living with him after we're married?'

'As long as you're there I don't mind where we live,' she said. 'And I couldn't leave my father alone—you're right. I'd already realised I was going to have to come back home if Gavin left. I'd booked on tomorrow's plane and I was going to wind up my affairs in Paris in due course.'

'You mean I wasted my energy rushing after you like this? You were coming home anyway tomorrow?'

Donna made a face at him, knowing he was teasing, seeing the happiness in his eyes, the lines of content in his face.

'At least you made yourself clear, at last,' she said.

'There are no more secrets, are there, Brodie?'

'One or two,' he said silkily, pulling her down on the bed again. 'But they aren't going to be secrets for much longer, darling. From now on we're not going to hide anything from each other.'

A thought flashed through her mind as she curved against him. 'But where did you get the money to buy the block of family shares?' she asked, and Brodie groaned.

'Didn't I tell you? I inherited my uncle's money automatically when he died. He didn't make a will, he wouldn't have wanted me to have it, but as I was his only living relative I got it all the same, so although he didn't intend it, he's responsible for bringing us together.' He laughed drily. 'He'd be furious if he knew!'

'Maybe he'd be pleased,' she protested. 'Give him the benefit of the doubt.'

Brodie eyed her through his lashes. 'If *you'd* given me that, we wouldn't have wasted two years.'

'I'm sorry, darling, I'm sorry,' she whispered, contrite, kissing his ear and moving on to his neck, her teeth softly grazing his skin.

Brodie's hands explored and she shivered with pleasure, her eyes closing. Very soon there would be no hiding-place, no pretences—only the intimacy and honesty of love.

ROMANCE

Variety is the spice of romance

Each month, Mills & Boon publish new romances. New stories about people falling in love. A world of variety in romance — from the best writers in the romantic world. Choose from these titles in March.

THE HEART OF THE MATTER Lindsay Armstrong
KING OF THE HILL Emma Goldrick
A MAN OF CONTRASTS Claudia Jameson
TOO SHORT A BLESSING Penny Jordan
HIDE AND SEEK Charlotte Lamb
TOO BAD TO BE TRUE Roberta Leigh
DON'T ASK FOR TOMORROW S. McCarthy
STORMY SPRINGTIME Betty Neels
SHADOWS IN THE LIMELIGHT Sandra K. Rhoades
RELATIVE STRANGERS Jessica Steele
*UNTAMED SANCTUARY Annabel Murray
*LOVE UPON THE WIND Sally Stewart

On sale where you buy paperbacks. If you require further information or have any difficulty obtaining them, write to: Mills & Boon Reader Service, PO Box 236, Thornton Road, Croydon, Surrey CR9 3RU, England.

*These two titles are available *only* from Mills & Boon Reader Service.

Mills & Boon
the rose of romance

ROMANCE

Next month's romances from Mills & Boon

Each month, you can choose from a world of variety in romance with Mills & Boon. These are the new titles to look out for next month.

WINTER SUNLIGHT Susan Alexander
THE GOOD-TIME GUY Rosemary Badger
THE ONE THAT GOT AWAY Emma Darcy
IMPULSIVE ATTRACTION Diana Hamilton
CASTLES IN THE AIR Rosemary Hammond
MASQUERADE MARRIAGE Flora Kidd
SHADOW FALL Rowan Kirby
NIGHT HEAT Anne Mather
AFTER THE LOVING Carole Mortimer
THERE IS NO TOMORROW Yvonne Whittal
*****HIGH COUNTRY** Sharron Cohen
*****HUNTER'S PREY** Jasmine Cresswell

Buy them from your usual paperback stockist, or write to: Mills & Boon Reader Service, P.O. Box 236, Thornton Rd, Croydon, Surrey CR9 3RU, England. Readers in Southern Africa — write to: Independent Book Services Pty, Postbag X3010, Randburg, 2125, S. Africa.

*These two titles are available *only* from Mills & Boon Reader Service.

Mills & Boon
the rose of romance

They were from different worlds...

...and yet nothing could keep them apart.

Elizabeth Parkins lived among the elegant surroundings in Chicago's North Shore.

Sam Winslow lived among the unfortunate souls destined to live in the city's decaying slums.

They would risk everything they believed in, just for the one chance to be together ... **WORLDWIDE**

Mills & Boon

YOU'RE INVITED TO ACCEPT **FOUR ROMANCES** AND A TOTE BAG **FREE!**

Acceptance card

| NO STAMP NEEDED | **Post to: Reader Service, FREEPOST, P.O. Box 236, Croydon, Surrey. CR9 9EL** |

Please note readers in Southern Africa write to:
Independant Book Services P.T.Y., Postbag X3010, Randburg 2125, S. Africa

YES! Please send me 4 free Mills & Boon Romances and my free tote bag – and reserve a Reader Service Subscription for me. If I decide to subscribe I shall receive 6 new Romances every month as soon as they come off the presses for £7.20 together with a FREE monthly newsletter including information on top authors and special offers, exclusively for Reader Service subscribers. There are no postage and packing charges, and I understand I may cancel or suspend my subscription at any time. If I decide not to subscribe I shall write to you within 10 days. Even if I decide not to subscribe the 4 free novels and the tote bag are mine to keep forever. I am over 18 years of age.   EP20R

NAME _____

(CAPITALS PLEASE)

ADDRESS _____

_____

_____

_____ POSTCODE _____